HONEYMOON FOR SEVEN

Honeymoon for Seven

ALFRED TOOMBS

PEOPLES BOOK CLUB, CHICAGO

To DAD—our favorite character

Chapter 1

I HAD the ring, the license and a date with the preacher at half past seven.

Connie was as radiant as the June sun which struck glittering highlights in her copper hair. Her tiny figure seemed just able to contain the excitement she was feeling as she listened to the plans for our wedding. Suddenly, she asked:

"Did you get a sitter?"

"A sitter?"

"You weren't planning to take the children to the wedding, were you?" she demanded.

I looked at the five young faces turned anxiously toward us.

"I thought they might enjoy it," I replied lamely. "Not many children see their parents get married."

"No," she said, shaking her head slowly, "I think you'd better get someone to look after them. Just this once, I'd rather not have a lot of children hanging on my neck."

I had taken it for granted that the children would come along. They had dogged our steps ever since Connie and I had met. Actually, they were our children in an individual, rather than a collective, sense. Connie was a young widow with two daughters: Cynthia, a prim, pretty young miss of seven who stared at the world with wide-eyed concern from behind her eye-glasses, and Claire, a doll-faced, curly-haired, uninhibited five-year-old imp. During the winter just past—the second we had spent in Florida—I had been converted into a grass widower, with three children in my custody. My son Larry was now a long-limbed, croak-voiced twelve-year-old; gentle Lynn, with the long golden hair, was nine, and Janie was a rugged little roly-poly of six.

At the time Connie and I had met, we were next-door neighbors in a quiet little village in central Florida. I had been doing all of the cooking, neckwashing and general housekeeping for my three children for nearly two years. Both my children and Connie's watched with considerable interest when they saw that my attentions to Connie were getting to be something above and beyond the call of neighborly duty. They carefully supervised the courtship and gave their consent to our betrothal only after due consideration. A marriage of this sort, Larry pointed out seriously, would be very much of a family affair.

About a month before the date Connie set for the wedding, we had both moved our families north. With my three children, I returned to the cottage in southern Maryland where we had been living during the summers. Connie, Claire and Cynthia had returned to stay at her family's home in Westchester County, New York. She had sorted through her possessions and had shipped those that she wanted in our new home. The day before she arrived for the wedding, my brother-in-law-to-be had pulled in with a rented auto trailer, loaded with boxes,

2

barrels and a crate containing a jet-black kitten named Emperor Jones.

Although new in his role as my brother-in-law, I could see that this kid had real talent. For he stood around drinking beer while I worked at unloading the trailer. Having consumed the last drop, he explained that he wouldn't be able to stay for the ceremony, got in his car and headed home.

This had left the Emperor Jones and me to explore the packing cases. I was particularly interested in their contents because I had not yet been able to locate Connie's electric mixer. I had told her candidly that, while her charms were dazzling and her virtues countless, she would have to realize that I was marrying her chiefly for her electric mixer. I had never felt that I could spare the money to buy one and, after two years of housekeeping, I was thoroughly tired of beating eggs, whipping cream and mixing cakes by hand. When I found the mixer in one of the newly arrived boxes, I plugged it in immediately. Then it was that I discovered that I had been duped. There were no mixing blades.

This was scarcely remarkable, because a large proportion of the treasures which Connie had sent didn't work. I supposed that she figured that, with a man around the house, she could get everything repaired. So I separated her possessions into two piles. The small pile included things that seemed to be in working order, while the large pile was made up of gadgets that didn't function. I put the electric mixer in the large pile with the waffle iron, the percolator, the flashlight with dead batteries and the broken can opener.

Connie was a professional sculptor and most of the other boxes contained clay, wire, chisels and assorted tools of the trade. One box contained several statues she had done. Among

3

them I recognized a half-life-sized self-portrait. It had been a long time since I had seen Connie and I gazed at the statue forlornly for a few minutes. Then I put it in the large pile, too.

During the morning of our wedding day, I labored like a Trojan char-woman, cleaning up the house. Finding that I still had a little time left before Connie was due, I decided to whip up a small but spectacular wedding feast. So I fried a chicken, made some salad and went to work with my old hand-powered egg beater, making a cake and muttering with every turn of the handle. I barely had time to get the flour cleaned off myself and the tables before I had to rush off to meet the bus bringing Connie, Claire and Cynthia.

It was a noisy reunion as the two sets of children greeted each other and their parents-to-be. But this disturbance was as nothing compared to the howls that went up when the children learned that they weren't to go to the wedding.

Larry said firmly that his father was not competent to get married without assistance and we finally consented to take him along to represent all of the children. Our next-door neighbors—a mother and grown daughter who had endured my family with saintly patience—agreed to watch the girls while we were away. I think they were so relieved at the thought that some moderating influence was being introduced into my household that they would have even loaned me money to pay the preacher.

We started out in the old Ford at dusk and headed for the preacher's house in Leonardtown, the county seat. We hadn't gone far before we got the feeling that we were being followed. A glance in the rear-view mirror showed that Larry's worthless beagle hound, Tonker, was racing along behind us. We had

4

never been able to teach Tonker anything whatsoever and, as a result, he did just what he wanted to do—and very few things he did not want to do. He had decided he was coming with us this evening. And unless I stopped the car, he would follow us down the road and get lost. Then I would spend my wedding night beating the bushes to find him. So we halted long enough to let him in the car. But when we got to the preacher's home, Connie—who loved every dog in the world, except Tonker—put down her dainty little 3-A.

"He'll have to stay in the car," she said firmly, and slammed the door in Tonker's face.

Tonker resented this bitterly. While we had no organ music as we marched toward the minister, the air was filled with the mournful, muted music of a howling hound. Larry served as best man, father-of-the-bride and our only witness. In the quiet of the minister's little study, the words of the wedding service seemed charged with such poetry and meaning that we were very nearly overcome by emotion as we kissed and turned to leave as man and wife.

The moon was low as we rode through the June-scented Maryland countryside. We were going straight home, of course, because where could we find anyone to watch our five children while we went away on a honeymoon?

Our cottage is on a little neck of land which becomes an island when the Potomac River and Dukehart Creek converge at high tide. It is connected to the mainland by a narrow cause-way, over which an automobile can pass. As we reached the road that leads into Dukehart Island, I pointed to a large tree.

"That's where we'll put it," I said.

"Put what?" asked Connie.

"The sign," I replied, " 'Welcome to Dukehart Island—Home of America's Fastest-Growing Little Family.' "

"It sure grew today," remarked Larry. "This morning I only had two sisters to bother about. Now I've got four of the little brats."

The girls were still awake when we reached the cottage. They were in a state of excitement and so we invited them to get up and share the wedding supper. After a time, we ordered them off to bed again. I opened a bottle of champagne and my bride sat with me on the front lawn for a while, sipping the wine and enjoying the blessed relief of being alone together. Then we decided to retire.

I had no sooner turned off the bedroom light than I heard a loud and insistent knock on the door of our room.

"What is it?" I called.

"Will you please make those little brats keep quiet?" Larry demanded. "A fellow can't get any sleep around here any more."

I got up and went to the room where the girls were sleeping.

"Please, kids," I said. "It's very late. Why don't you get to sleep?"

"I was jes' tellin' Claire about all my dolls," said Janie, my youngest.

"That could take quite a while," I replied, recalling that she owned two dozen of them. "Why not save it for tomorrow?"

"Where's Mommy?" demanded Connie's youngest, Claire.

"In bed," I said.

"I wanna sleep with her."

"No, dear. You sleep in your own bed."

"Tell Mommy to come here," Claire insisted.

"What do you want, dear?" I asked. "I'll get it for you."

"I want Mommy."

"No, you go to sleep," I said firmly.

Back in our bedroom, I turned off the light and climbed into bed. Suddenly, the quiet of the night was shattered by a piercing wail.

"Mommeeeee. . . ."

Connie jumped up as if she had been stung by a wasp. I sat blinking at the light until she returned.

"Claire wanted a drink of water," Connie explained, and turned the light off once more.

"Does she always ask for it that loud?" I said, and Connie laughed.

At this point, Tonker began to bark and scratch at the front door. I started to get up.

"Where are you going?" my bride demanded.

"Got to let the dog in," I explained. "Or else he'll keep that racket up all night."

On my way through the dark living room, I stumbled over Janie's doll carriage and, falling, cracked my head against something that felt very much like another, harder head.

It was Larry's.

"What in thunder are you doing out here?" I demanded.

"I can't sleep," he wailed. "Those darn girls keep whispering. Besides, you hurt my head just then."

"Get an aspirin and go to bed," I snapped.

But our house continued to be about as peaceful as Saturday night in the courthouse square. Cynthia fell out of bed. There were three separate reports of boogie men in the girls' room which I had to investigate. Tonker chased the Emperor Jones up on a closet shelf and sat there barking at him.

Quiet finally settled over the house, but I still lay sleepless

7

and quivering. I was haunted by the thought that, while Claire had aroused us three times to bring her drinking water, she had gotten us up only twice to take her to the bathroom.

So all I could do was to lie there, waiting for her to even up the score.

Chapter 2

I W A S awakened early the next morning by the sound of a kitten purring on the pillow beside me. I opened my eyes to find the Emperor Jones sleeping next to my ear. Tonker was curled up next to Jones, on Connie's pillow, and I was happy to see that they had patched up their differences of the night before. Then I glanced sleepily around the room and saw curly-haired Claire sitting in a corner, sucking her thumb and glowering resentfully at me. I glowered back at her briefly and then, noting that Connie was still asleep, decided I would try to catch another forty winks.

But it wasn't long before Claire climbed up on the bed and began to shake her mother. Connie slept on while three other girls piled into bed, but when Larry appeared she awakened to find herself in a standing-room-only crowd.

"Oh my gosh!" she wailed drowsily, taking a quick look around.

"Some relatives of ours," I said. "Along for the honeymoon."

"Gee," she said. "Are you sure they're all here? Let's see, one, two, three, four. . . . Somebody's missing."

"It's me," yelled Larry. "I'm under the bed."

"That makes five," Connie laughed.

"Quintuplets," I pointed out. "Now we know what the Dionnes felt like."

"But we've only been married one day," she sighed. "Now whatever do you suppose these children want?"

"Breakfast," I said, moving a couple of muscles as if I were going to jump up and fix it, just as I had been doing for my own family every weary morning, it seemed, since the dawn of time.

"You stay here," Connie muttered, with an understandable lack of enthusiasm. "I'll fix them some toast."

"We want pancakes," Larry rasped.

Connie raised her head from the pillow, opened one eye and looked at me.

"Is he kidding?" she asked. "Do you eat stuff like that for breakfast?"

"Sure," I replied. "Why not?"

"I don't eat breakfast at all," she said sadly.

We both were hit by the same noble impulse and threw back the covers simultaneously and swung our feet around to the floor.

"I'll fix breakfast," I said, "you stay here and sleep."

"No," she said, "you deserve a rest, I'll fix it."

We looked at each other for a minute, then spoke together. "No sense in both of us getting up."

So we both dived back into bed.

"Maybe the children could fix their own breakfast," Connie said. "I bet Lynn is a good cook."

"She can't even get toast brown," Larry protested.

I made a quick leap out of bed, grabbed my bathrobe and started for the kitchen.

"You stay here until I get the coffee fixed," I told Connie. "Wedding present for the bride."

The children came racing out and began to set the table. Claire and Cynthia hung back from my children and were regarding the scene with suspicion.

"What would you girls like for breakfast?" I asked. "Some cereal?"

"Are we having cereal again?" Cynthia demanded, peering up at me over the top of her glasses.

"What do you mean, *again?*" I laughed. "This is your first breakfast here."

"Mommy doesn't *make* us eat cereal," Claire explained, putting her arms around my waist and turning her pretty little face up to me coquettishly. " 'Cept sometimes, we eat it anyway."

"What kind of cereal are you girls having?" Cynthia asked.

"Shedded wheat," Janie replied seriously.

"Okay," said Cynthia, "but take the cream off my milk."

"Oh, Cynthia," Janie protested. "I don't like skinned milk."

I was anxious to get my two new daughters off on the right foot. They looked just a little uneasy and I knew only too well that my ways of housekeeping were not Connie's ways. I decided that, after all, pancakes would be a pretty good breakfast to put the little girls in good humor. I went to work over the griddle and before long I had a stack of cakes ready.

Then it was that Claire looked at me coyly and said:

"I don't 'special like pancakes."

"Why not?" I asked with concern.

"Least, I don't like the shyrup," Claire said.

"Well, why don't you eat your pancakes without syrup?" I asked.

"But Al," Claire protested. "What good are pancakes without shyrup?"

"You've got me there," I replied gravely. "Maybe you'd like an egg, instead."

"Oh, Claire," said Janie, deciding to be helpful. "Daddy fixes so good eggs. You'll jes' love the 'oaks."

Both of my new daughters continued to look dubious at the prospect of an egg. But I was determined to please them, so I asked:

"How about some toast and jelly?"

"Okay," said Cynthia. "But please don't put any butter on my toast."

"How about you, Claire?" I asked.

"I'm jes' tryin' to decide whether to have toast or not toast," she explained.

By the time the meal was over, I was a thoroughly shaken man.

"Guess I've got a whole new set of whims to learn," I told Connie, as we sipped coffee. "But wait until you start trying to cook for my kids!"

The girls stacked the breakfast dishes up in the sink for us, and when Connie saw the size of the pile she looked dismayed.

"Sure you haven't been saving these up all week?" she asked.

"Nope—they're all from breakfast. We are seven—remember?"

"Gee, we wouldn't dirty this many in a week at home," she said sadly.

The children went tootling off. Connie and I watched out

of the window as my youngsters began to show their new sisters around the place. Everyone seemed to be happy and cheerful and I gave Connie a little hug as we saw them scamper by.

"Well, so far we're just one big happy family," I observed.

When we had at last reduced our mountain of dishes to a molehill, I followed my children's example and led Connie out for a tour of the place. The points of interest were few, but I described them with all of the enthusiasm of a Moslem talking about Mecca.

"Before you," I said, "lies the historic Potomac River, five miles wide and a little salty here. The cliffs you see on the other side are the Virginia shore and just up the river was George Washington's boyhood home."

"He didn't throw the silver dollar across here, did he?" Connie asked.

"Nope, but you are married to a man who once swam across the river here," I said. "And I doubt if Washington ever did that."

She looked impressed and I continued my spiel.

"On all sides of you, you will find lots of fresh air, which is our principal commodity. We also have an orchard, including apple trees, pear trees and a couple of peach trees that never bear fruit. On your left, you will see my vegetable garden and that fenced-in area among the weeds is my chicken pen."

"If you wanted to get away from it all," she said wonderingly, "this would be the place to come."

"It's a real jumping-off place," I agreed.

"I love it," she said wonderingly. "I love it."

This was a great load off my mind. Actually, I didn't know how Connie was going to take it. There was only one house, other than ours, on the five-acre island. Both were little summer cottages, drab and a little tumbled down. As Connie had noted, we were about as far from civilization as one could get and the facilities which awaited her were just a little better than primitive.

The little cottage in which we were living belonged to my father. It had been my summer home in boyhood days and it was here, after my return from the war a couple of years earlier, that I had taken refuge with the three children which circumstance had left in my exclusive care. Since I was a writer, I could still earn my livelihood this far from the city.

For my children and myself, the place had been adequate. Our life had been like a big camping trip. But now that I had a wife, I was not sure how the rugged country manner of living was going to be. And so, when Connie said again "I love it," I heaved a sigh of relief and hoped that she knew what she was getting into.

We walked back to the cottage after a few minutes and my bride asked:

"What shall we have for dinner? It should be something special."

"It will be something special, if I just have someone else cook it for me," I said. "After two years of eating my own cooking, I'm a little tired of it."

"So, what shall we have?"

"How about deviled crabs?"

"Sounds swell," she said. "And what else?"

"Lima beans and sweet potatoes."

She looked at me with those great big beautiful bride eyes and said:

14

"Gee, it's wonderful to have a husband who knows how to plan meals. Now, what about dessert?"

"Apple brown Betty," I said without hesitation.

"Okay," she said. "Where do you keep the crab meat?"

"In the river," I replied. "I haven't caught the crabs, yet."

"Can I help you?" she asked eagerly.

"Sure," I said. "We've got an extra net."

"Do the crabs bite?"

"Sure."

"Maybe I'd better make the dessert," she replied. "Do you have some apples?"

"Apples you'll find in the orchard," I told her.

"On the trees?" she asked incredulously. "How do I get 'em down?"

"Use a small child," I suggested.

"And what about the beans? Could I phone down to the village for a few things like that?"

"What village?" I countered, "and what phone?"

"Oh, I forgot," she said.

"I've got limas growing in the garden. Lynn can help you pick them. She's my helpful child."

"And I suppose the potatoes are still on the bushes, too," Connie asked.

"They grow under the ground," I replied. "I'll dig some up for you after a while."

"Are you teasing me?" she demanded. "I didn't know you really grew these things."

"Where did you think they came from?"

"I always just went to the store and bought them."

It was some time later when I walked into the house with

a bucket full of crabs and found Connie contemplating a half-peeled apple with a look of unmixed distaste.

"There's a worm in it," she said.

"Just one?" I asked, and laughed.

"I don't know. I saw one in the first apple and that was enough."

"Aw, just cut around it," I suggested.

"I'm afraid of worms," Connie whispered.

"Okay," I snorted. "Wait until I get these crabs steaming and then I'll help with the apples."

The rest of the afternoon, the family spent working with Connie. We helped her pick crabs, peel apples and potatoes and shell lima beans. We had a great time, teaching the city-bred branch of the family the facts of country living.

As dinner time approached, I strolled out to the front porch to enjoy a moment that I had been awaiting for many long months. I was going to sit down in a rocking chair and have someone cook dinner for me. I had gotten off only a couple of rocks, however, before my reverie was interrupted by a call from the kitchen.

"Hey," Connie demanded plaintively, "how do I turn on this stove?"

"There's a pair of pliers on the shelf over the stove," I yelled. "The handles on the stove are broken."

A few moments later, she called again:

"You better come here, if you want any dinner. I can't work the stove."

I went into the kitchen, fiddled around with the ancient stove until it warmed up and was just about to leave when I saw that Connie was looking for something on the shelves.

"Where's the sugar?" she asked.

"In the can marked salt," I explained.

"And I suppose there's salt in the can marked sugar," she laughed.

"No," I replied, "flour's in the sugar can."

Just then, one of the battered roly-poly saucepans with which I had struggled throughout my housekeeping career rolled over suddenly and spilled hot water on the floor.

"That spills if you fill it too high," I explained.

"Where's the mop?" she asked.

"Durned if I know," I said. "Larry was using it to push the rowboat around the other day."

Connie gave me a baffled look.

"Where did you get this water, anyway?" I asked suspiciously.

"Out of the spigot, naturally," she replied.

"You can't use water out of the spigot for drinking or cooking," I explained. "It has a funny taste. Use the water in the bucket. We get that from the deep well next door."

Suddenly, I found myself confronted with a very unhappy little bride.

"All of this," she said slowly, "is a little too much for me to learn in one easy lesson."

"I guess it is," I admitted. "I'll cook the dinner. You just fix us a drink."

"Okay," she said. "Where's your still?"

"I buy liquor at the store," I said.

"Thank Heaven, I was afraid I was going to have to chop some kindling for the boiler," she said.

It wasn't long before I got things under control in the kitchen, although I did have a little trouble remembering to double the recipes that I was accustomed to preparing for four. I was still dreaming wistfully of the dinner that someone else was going to cook for me when Larry raced through the kitchen.

"What you doin', Pop?" he demanded.

"Playing parcheesi," I said brightly. "What's it look like?"

"Same old racket," he called out, as he sped away. "Only now you're doin' it for seven."

Chapter 3

O U R S had long been two hearts that beat as one so we had no problem there. But now we were trying to get our two families to live as one—and this was a problem.

The household which I had managed for my children never had been put on any sort of schedule. We had run a continuous rat race and, at the end of each lap, had all paused long enough to eat, sleep and bandage our wounds. Then we took off again.

We never had a very exact dinner hour, for example. Sometimes we ate at six and sometimes at eight. The dinner hour was determined by such external factors as how long it took me to capture the *pièce de résistance,* which of my temperamental kitchen appliances broke down or whether I felt like making a production number out of the evening meal. It must be understood that I had never been content to be a mere can-of-beans or salmon salad chef. I had taken cooking seriously. Maybe I was just trying to show off, but I was by way of becoming the poor man's Escoffier. Still our meals, while spectacular, were seldom served on time.

Connie, being a woman of good sense, took a dim view of our variable dinner hour. To her, the evening meal was something which was to be served promptly at six o'clock and forgotten about as speedily as possible. Other questions in connection with dinner were secondary to her.

When I would marvel at the way she got dinner on the table on time every night, she explained:

"It's just that I don't try to win a Pulitzer Prize with every dinner, like you do."

Since it had become obvious, on the first day of our married life, that Connie was not going to be able immediately to divine the mysteries surrounding the preparation of a meal on Dukehart Island, I had done all the cooking so far. This meant we were eating my style—good, but not on time. The first dinner was only half an hour late. The second dinner was an hour and a half late, but I felt that there had been extenuating circumstances. I knew how long it would take me to catch enough fish for four of us—but how was I to know that it would take twice as long to get enough for seven? Came the third day, and Connie asked pleasantly:

"What time will we have dinner?"

"Silly girl!" I replied. "How would I know?"

"It would be nice if we could have dinner early and get the girls to bed," she said. "Maybe I could help you."

"If you like."

"What are you going to have?"

"I thought I'd make a blue cheese soufflé and baked potatoes. Then we could have broccoli with hollandaise sauce and for dessert, have *baba au rhum*."

She whistled.

"How about just having hot dogs, canned corn and a store cake?" she suggested. "I could get that on the table by six, myself."

"Here, the hens lay eggs practically for free," I replied. "But they won't lay hot dogs."

"Well," she said and sighed. "I love your soufflé. But it's two o'clock now and you'd better get started."

Although this irony was not lost upon me, it did not register with the hens. I needed eight eggs for the repast and by five o'clock, the layers had produced only seven. It wasn't until five-thirty that a reluctant hen yielded up the final egg. Dinner was going to be late again. Connie offered to help with the preliminaries on the hollandaise sauce and, while I was busy with something else, she opened her own cook book and started to work. When I got around to checking on her progress, I found her dumping three beaten egg yolks into the melted butter.

"Hey," I protested. "You're doing it backwards. You pour the butter slowly over the eggs."

She pointed to a line in her cook book and replied:

"My cook book says to do it this way."

I reached for my cook book, pointed to the recipe and said:

"My book says the eggs go in first."

"Well," she shrugged. "It's too late now."

"You better throw that book away," I said. "It's obviously out of date. If you cook by a thing like that, we'll all wind up with scurvy."

"You're a funny man," she said, turning her mouth up to be kissed.

Bells rang, lights flashed and the angels sang. When I re-

21

laxed my embrace, the broccoli was boiling over. Dinner was only an hour late and the sauce, by any recipe, was a success.

"Claire, don't you jes' love my daddy's dinners?" Janie asked.

"'Specially the holiday sauce," Claire said, looking at me demurely out of the corners of her eyes.

"You little girls will have to get ready for bed now," Connie said.

"But, Mommy," Claire protested, "we jes' on'y finished eatin'."

"When dinner's this late, you have to go to bed right away," said Connie quietly.

Claire's protest was violent and lengthy, but Connie remained serene. Janie, somewhat more accustomed to leaving the table and jumping in bed, did not join in until she saw what a good thing Claire was making of the issue. Even when she joined the rebellion, Connie remained calm and shepherded the wailing pair off to bed without so much as raising her voice.

"I'm sorry about dinner being so late," I told her when we had finished the dishes.

"Oh, that's all right," she replied. "We just do things differently. But we'll get so we use the same recipes."

Connie and I did not use the same recipes for handling children, either. She was a disciple of the modern, let-'em-alone school of child psychology and she had a natural, easy way with children. I had given the modern school a brief trial with my children, but I just couldn't take it. I was by inclination too much of a disciplinarian. Connie admitted that she thought her girls could do with a little—not too much—of the sort of firm treatment I handed out to my brood. And I knew that mine could use a lot of the kind of loving patience that she gave.

When loving patience had succeeded in getting all of the girls to bed, my bride and I strolled out into the front yard, hand in hand, to contemplate the beauties of nature.

At the water's edge, Connie's tiny figure was silhouetted against the twilight sky. A sliver of moon was visible in the azure and a golden star or two twinkled at us.

"Like it here?" I asked.

"It's heavenly," she replied.

Then she saw the moon.

"Let's make a wish on the moon," she whispered, like a child who was suggesting a new game.

"Okay," I said, and put my arm around her. We both took a deep breath and wished with all our might.

"What did you wish for?" she asked.

"Something for us," I said. "But if I told you, it might not come true, might it?"

"I guess not," she said. "But let's remember this. And after we've been married for a year, we'll tell each other what our wishes were and see how we made out."

"All right," I said, drawing her close enough to kiss.

"I love you," Connie said.

There was a loud groan behind us.

"Boy, how corny can you get?" rasped Larry.

"Go get lost, junior," I suggested.

"Hey, Pop, you better quit that lovey-dovey stuff and come see what those little brats are doing in the house," he said.

As soon as we walked into the living room, we heard Claire's voice:

"Mommeeee. . . ."

"What is it?" Connie asked.

"I wanna drinka water."

23

Without a murmur of protest, Connie took a glass of water into the bedroom. Things were quiet for a short time, then we heard Janie call:

"Daddeee. . . ."

"What?" I asked.

"I wanna drinka water."

"You know I don't give you water after you've gone to bed," I barked.

"Claire gets it," she wailed.

"Well, that doesn't mean you're going to."

"Let me get some for her," Connie said. "Maybe she's really thirsty."

"She's not thirsty," I insisted. "She's just trying to get into the act."

I glanced up to see Claire's face peering around the edge of the door. Her curly-brown hair was tousled and her lower lip was stuck out in a pout.

"Mommy," she said, "you forgot bed-time candy."

Connie rose and walked to the kitchen again.

"Bed-time candy!" I demanded when she returned. "What kind of racket is that?"

"Oh, I always give them a little piece of candy when they go to bed. They're better about going to sleep, then."

"Gee, that's terrible," I said.

"Why?" she asked in surprise.

"Ruins their teeth—spoils the children."

"Oh, I don't think a little spoiling will hurt them."

I shook my head in wonder.

"You're the most patient mother I ever saw."

"I only wish I could be more patient."

"I've never seen you get cross with your children."

"You will, just wait."

Then, Janie called out.

"Daddeee. . . ."

"What now?"

"I gotta go to the bathroom."

"You might as well have given her the drink," Connie laughed.

"Well, go ahead," I yelled at Janie.

"But I'm afraid."

"Afraid of what?"

"Claire says there's a boogie man in the closet."

"All of a sudden, the house is full of boogie men," I grumbled. "Never heard of one around here until a week ago."

Then, walking into the girls' room, I turned on the light for Janie. When she was ready to jump back in bed, she said:

"I'm thirsty."

"Me, too," said Claire.

I stomped out of the room, returned with two glasses of water and two more pieces of candy. When they had finished this repast, I said sternly:

"Now both of you little girls go to the bathroom again and then brush your teeth. After that, I don't want to hear another peep out of you."

When I walked back into the living room, Connie was smiling at me.

"How am I doing?" I asked.

"What cook book did you get that one from?" she asked.

"Just my paternal instincts," I explained.

Early the next morning, the two little girls set off to play in the sand on the beach. I happened to be walking by on the bank above them some time later and I stopped to listen.

"Now Mommy has five children," Claire said.

"Yeah, Claire, but she only laid two of 'em," said Janie, who knew all about chickens.

There was a moment's silence and I moved a little closer.

"Claire, suppose you were havin' a baby?" Janie speculated.

"How could I?" Claire demanded. "I can't even tell time."

It was at this point that I noticed the girls were playing in the sand with what appeared to be some spoons out of Connie's best silver set. When I got back to the house, I paused to report the snatches of conversation I had picked up and then said to Connie:

"I think they've got your best spoons down there."

"Oh, they can't hurt them," she said casually, "they're solid silver."

"It's a good thing I asked you. I was just about to give them hell."

Early that afternoon, our neighbors offered Connie a ride to the grocery store in Leonardtown and she left the children in my care. She hadn't been gone long before the children decided that they would put on a circus.

Larry appeared first, attired in some of my sports clothes. I noted with dismay that they fitted him pretty well. Larry was usually obsessed with one subject or another and at this moment, it was the radio. He spent most of his time listening to disc jockey programs and addressed everyone as if he were speaking to the great, unseen audience.

But, as barker for the circus, he had dropped his gentle tones and was broadcasting without benefit of transmitter.

"You want to buy a ticket, mister?" he asked, standing barely two feet away from me and shouting at the top of his voice.

"Sure, iron lungs, when's the show start?"

26

"Soon as we get a crowd," he yelled.

I went into the house a few minutes later and found four giggling girls in our bedroom. They had pulled most of Connie's clothes out of the closet and were attiring themselves. Great quantities of powder and perfume were being scattered about.

"What's Connie going to say about this?" I asked.

"Oh, Mommy doesn't care," Cynthia assured me.

I looked at them dubiously, but then decided that it was just my nasty disciplinarian nature which made me want to spoil their fun. So I withdrew.

The circus parade was still winding its way across our yard when Connie returned from the store. The girls were dressed as clowns, lion tamers and fat ladies, but when Connie stepped out of the car they broke ranks and ran toward her—tripping over their long skirts.

When I got close enough to my bride to kiss her, the suspicion grew upon me that something was amiss. Her expression, as she looked at the girls, was blank—a little too blank, I felt. Her nose was twitching like a rabbit's and, without a word, she marched toward the house.

"Claire, you've got lifstip all over Connie's blouse," Janie shouted.

I grabbed the groceries and followed the crowd to the house. As I walked into the living room, I heard the sound of Connie's voice raised in anger.

"Claire and Cynthia, I've told you never, never to play with my clothes," she was saying. "And never, never to touch my perfume."

"It's my fault, I guess, dear," I said. "I should have stopped them. But I thought it was the sort of thing you didn't care about."

"Didn't care about them ruining my things?" she said.

"Guess I was just trying to use a recipe out of your book," I said sadly.

It wasn't long before Connie had everything restored to good order. I helped her put away the groceries and then I asked: "What'll I cook for dinner?"

"I'm going to cook dinner," she said firmly. "And I'm going to use your cook book."

It was a wonderful dinner. Roast beef, with yorkshire pudding, stuffed baked potatoes and a lemon meringue pie. It was just the sort of dinner that I might have knocked myself out to cook, all right.

And it was only two hours late.

Chapter 4

THE honeymoon cottage to which I had brought my bride and our ready-made family was not the sort of place of which the minstrels sing. It was so down at the heels, in fact, that I had proposed to Connie we should postpone our wedding for a couple of weeks until I could get some serious remodeling done. But she said she'd rather be there while the work was going on, even if it did mean putting up with some inconveniences for a couple of weeks.

The first rooms of the cottage had been built some 25 years before Connie and I were married. My father had hired a carpenter to put up a modest, three-room, week-end retreat. Dad didn't like the job that the carpenter did and had been trying to improve upon it ever since. The result was a rambler —it rambled first in this direction and then in the other, as Dad added bedrooms, subtracted porches and divided the sitting room. At the time of our marriage, there were seven rooms, more or less, and Dad was still going strong. I always had the feeling that he was hurrying to add another room to the place before the ones he had finished should collapse.

29

Dad resolutely refused to hire any artisans or mechanics and did all the work on the place himself. He regarded carpenters, plumbers and electricians with hostility and suspicion, because they would never fall in with the fantastic schemes he devised to get the job done cheaply. Sometimes, when he would be working around the part of the house that the original carpenter had built, I would hear him mutter angrily:

"Darn fool carpenter. Put enough nails in here to build a whole new room."

This would mean that Dad had come across some piece of timber which had been nailed in place to stay. He never put things in that way himself, since everything he did was only temporary. He would drive a light nail half way into a board and explain that he was going to take it out again soon.

As a result, everthing in the house was subject to change without notice. It was possible to walk out of a door and return an hour later to find that Dad had boarded up the opening and had cut a new doorway through what had once been a window.

Dad never quite finished anything he started.

"This is only temporary," he would explain, hanging a door that was just slightly too small for its frame. "I'll put in a new door when I can get one."

Two years later, the small door would still be there.

The outstanding exhibit of this kind was the huge, double-sized sink, circa 1908, which Dad had installed temporarily 25 years ago.

Dad was a construction engineer and, often, changes were made in the cottage merely to utilize some odd or end of building material which he had acquired in the practice of his profession. He was forever picking up sets of three windows for which no mates existed anywhere in the world, or some exotic paneling ripped out of an old mansion. When he happened upon such windfalls, he would immediately substitute them for something that was in the house or build a new room to accommodate them. Once, a heavy double door, seven feet long and five feet wide, floated up on our beach. The door was evidently out of the grand salon on some river steamer. Dad had new glass cut for the door, ripped out half of the front of the house and created a new entrance to the living room. I suggested that he put a steamboat whistle up in the eaves and he said he would, if one floated ashore.

The result was that neither the doors, windows nor decor of any two rooms in the house matched. But if you only looked at one part of the house at a time, it didn't look too bad.

To marry me, Connie had left one of those neat towns in suburban New York where, for a small down payment and a mortgage on the best twenty years of one's life, all of the comforts of civilization can be had. Actually she had led a varied life. As a teen-ager, she had danced in a Chester Hale chorus. To help pay her college expenses, she had worked as a manicurist. As a young wife in depression years, she had maintained a home in an apartment over a garage on a budget of eight dollars a week. She had later earned a living for herself and her daughters as a professional sculptor. For reasons which were never quite clear to me, she had turned down a proposal from a millionaire in order to marry me—or, to be more accurate, to marry us.

Nothing—but nothing—in her life had quite prepared her for the exigencies of life in the cottage on Dukehart, however.

Whatever dismay she may have felt when she saw the drab brown paneling of the living room, the doors that neither fitted nor matched and the unpapered bedrooms, she showed none of it. With that blend of clairvoyance and optimism which comes as part of the equipment on a deluxe model woman, she announced immediately that she saw great possibilities in the place.

Every door knob, electric switch and plumbing fixture in the house had its own idiosyncrasy and she set about bravely to learn them all. I warned her that it would take years of practice to be able to live a full life in this house.

"It won't be much of a job to replace this, will it?" she would ask cheerily when I'd find her struggling with a window that refused to open or a door that wouldn't stay closed.

Usually I would look at her with surprise, because it had never been our practice to replace things simply because they didn't work.

"I guess I'm just not very practical," she would apologize.

"If you'd been practical," my reply would be, "you'd never have married me."

But in an impractical kind of way, Connie *was* practical. When she saw a room that needed to be papered, she got out a catalogue and began to select the pattern she wanted. When she saw something that needed paint, she began to study color charts. Dad and I had to spend a lot of time explaining to her why it was that she couldn't go ahead and do any of the things she wanted to do.

My father had turned the place over to me after the war with the understanding that, while it was still his house, I was to be responsible for maintenance and improvements. This had been comparatively simple while I was camping out there with my children. I had done the maintenance work myself and had made no improvements. I was dedicated to The

Simple Life. To me, this meant spending as little money as possible, raising as much of my own food as I could and performing with my own hands the services which normal people hired done. I dressed in left-over Army clothes which fitted in well with the left-over look of the house. For a time, I refused even to own an automobile and we traveled around the countryside on bicycles.

But, shortly before I married Connie, I had bought my father's pre-war Ford. I did this with misgivings, because I felt that this luxury would make a Consumer of me again. Like the first drink, I was sure that others would follow.

I had spent so much time saving money that I had little time left in which to earn money. So, now that I was faced with the necessity of making large-scale changes in the house, it was necessary to turn to Dad for financial help.

It was the matter of giving Connie a bath which brought the issue to a head. Shortly before our marriage, I had made some casual remark about the arrival of a new bathtub. The day after the wedding, I found Connie wandering around the house with a towel, a cake of soap and a puzzled look.

"Where's the tub?" she asked.

I led her to the back of the house, pointed out the window and replied:

"Out there in the yard. We haven't uncrated it yet."

"But what'll I do for a bath?" she asked plaintively.

"Why don't you take a shower?" I suggested, and led her to the dark little stall where Dad had set up a temporary shower for us eight years before.

I started to explain how to turn on and regulate the kerosene hot-water heater—a job which really called for a licensed stationary engineer—but Connie didn't seem to be listening.

33

"I can't stand going in close places like that," she said.

"Why not?" I asked.

"I've got one of those phobias. Besides, there might be a spider in there."

I looked at her quizzically.

"Maybe I'd better take my bath in the kitchen sink," she said.

This seemed to me to be one of her typically practical solutions and so I shrugged and left her to her own devices. A few minutes later, however, I heard a shriek from the kitchen and rushed in to find my bride seated in a puddle of suds in the oversized sink and looking very mad.

"What happened?" I asked.

"Sat on the steel wool," she explained.

The sight of the girl of my dreams, reduced to elbowing pots and pans out of the way in order to get a bath, disturbed me to such an extent that I resolved to get the house remodeled immediately, so that the bathtub could be installed.

Although there were many obstacles in the way of achieving this laudable purpose, the two which turned out to be most nearly insurmountable were my father and myself. Dad resolutely refused to hire workmen for the job and I was in no financial position to do so myself. Since I was still fondly living the role of The Brave Pioneer, I fell in with his plan to do the work ourselves.

Connie and I sat up evenings making plans for remodeling. We presented them to Dad and he agreed to lend me money to buy the materials. I finally prevailed upon him to allow me to hire a carpenter to help us, provided the man would work under his close supervision. This would preclude the possibility

34

that too much of the job would be done in a permanent fashion, so it was all right with Dad.

Dad picked up an ancient carpenter on the road one day and the man agreed to help on the job. Then Dad announced that he would take a two-week vacation to build the addition to the house. We were going to add two bedrooms, another bathroom and also remodel the interior.

On the week end when work was scheduled to begin, Dad arrived at the house late Friday night. He usually drove over the causeway, but this time he was on foot.

"Where's your car?" I asked.

"Over on the mainland," he replied.

"What's the matter?" I demanded. "Is the tide up over our road?"

"Nope. The lumber truck ran off the road. You better come help us dig it out."

Ten tons of truck and lumber were mired down in the ditch and it took the best part of the night to straighten out the mess. The next day was devoted to hauling lumber on to the island on our backs. On Sunday, I set out to locate Dad's carpenter and make sure that he was going to report for work the next day. When I finally tracked the old man down, he was in a bar room and was, I judged, about eighty proof. The bar tender explained that the carpenter was on a "hot," as the local expression goes, and cheerfully estimated that it would take ten days to dehydrate him. I scouted around the country, but all of the other carpenters I could locate were either already engaged or already drunk.

"Well," Dad said happily, when I broke the news, "I guess we'll just have to do it ourselves, after all."

Our first step was to pour some concrete foundations for the addition, so I began huffing and puffing around with ninety-pound bags of cement. Even with the aid of a wheelbarrow, it was all I could do to move one bag at a time.

Dad and I were in the midst of a conference on the shady side of the house when I heard a tremendous uproar on the other side. Suddenly, Larry came tearing around the house toward us. Immediately behind him came the wheelbarrow, with three bags of cement stacked on it, and it was traveling at a fast clip. I blinked as I saw the large, economy-size youth who was pushing it at a dead run.

"Who's that?" I asked Dad, as he whizzed by.

"That's Jack," Dad explained. "He's spending the week end next door."

The shouting grew louder again. When the wheelbarrow came around this time, it had not only the three bags of cement on it, but Larry and Claire as well. They proceeded around the place with undiminished speed.

"I'll trip him, next time around," I told Dad. "That'll be three sacks of cement I won't have to wrestle with."

But next time, Jack stopped the wheelbarrow and paused for breath. As the children ran away, he looked us over for a minute.

"Whatcha doin', Colonel?" he said to my father. "Fixin' to build somethin'?"

Dad introduced me to Jack and I asked:

"Mind if I take that cement off the wheelbarrow?"

" 'Deed not," replied the man mountain. "Want me to run the rest of it around here for you?"

I agreed with enthusiasm and Jack stayed on for the rest of the day, helping us with the job. He performed prodigious

36

feats of strength and never seemed to get tired. Jack told me that he was eighteen years old, was six feet, two inches tall and weighed about two hundred and fifty pounds. He was a nephew of the lady who lived next door, but this was his first visit to the island. Before the day was over, Dad had hired him to help us out on the job.

When I went in the house, I broke the news to Connie.

"He's going to eat over here with us," I said. "But he'll sleep over at his aunt's house."

"Let's see," she said weakly, "that'll make nine of us for meals, won't it?"

"If I've got time, I'll help with the cooking," I said.

"I'll probably need a little help," she said.

Suddenly, I saw a look of alarm cross her face.

"Hey," she squealed, "what happened to the sink?"

"Dad took it out," I replied. "Said it was in the way or something. He's going to put a little wash basin in there for you—just temporarily, of course."

"Now I haven't got anything to take a bath in," she said. "How long's it going to be before the bathroom's ready?"

"Gosh, I don't know. We didn't make much progress today."

She looked at me wonderingly.

"You know," she said, "I'm glad we didn't wait until this was done before we got married."

"Why?" I asked. "You enjoying this?"

"No," she said. "But if we'd waited, I might have been too old."

Chapter 5

*D*AD was up early the next morning. My muscles were aching from the exertions of the day before as I staggered out to the kitchen to start breakfast for the working party. I had barely begun when the room filled up with Jack.

"Whatcha cookin', Doc?" he beamed.

"Breakfast," I said grumpily. "How'll you have your egg?"

"Oh, I like 'em fried," he replied. "But don't get 'em brown around the edges."

"I said 'egg,' singular," I answered. "We're having pancakes, too."

"With sausage?" he demanded eagerly.

"Nope, no sausage," I replied.

"You ought to get yourself a pig," he said. "Then we could have sausage for breakfast every day. Mal de plume."

"How's that?" I asked.

"Mal de plume," repeated Jack. "That's French—I guess."

"What does it mean?" I asked idly, as I flipped some pancakes.

38

"Oh, just mal de plume."

"I don't get it," I said.

"Nobody ever understands what I say," Jack replied. "Even when I speak English."

I put a dozen pancakes and a couple of fried eggs down on the table for the two of them and turned back to the stove to cook my own breakfast. By the time mine was ready, Dad had hurried out to get started. But Jack was still sitting there with an empty plate and an expectant look. I gave him my egg and cakes and went back to the kitchen to mix up more batter.

Just as I was about to eat a pancake, Dad hove into view demanding:

"You fellows going to spend the morning eating?"

So I gulped a glass of milk and trotted out after Jack, who was still looking as hungry as I felt.

"Hope we have lunch early," he said.

During the morning, I began to get a little clearer impression of our carpenter's helper, Jack the Giant. He let me know that he had something of a reputation in high school as a wit and clown. I began to suspect that he affected the role of the feckless, confused oaf to draw laughing attention to himself. Behind this front, there seemed to lie a warm and engaging person who had a great deal more native intelligence than he wanted anyone to recognize.

Jack talked to me about his abbreviated high-school career, which he had terminated for reasons that seemed good and sufficient. He had gone to the same high school as his older brother, a star schoolboy football player who was currently an athlete in the employ of a southern university. Being even larger than his brother, Jack had been put under considerable

39

pressure to play on the high-school football team, too. But, like Ferdinand the Bull, Jack just wanted to smell the flowers. He didn't like to play football.

"Too rough," he said simply.

During summer vacations, Jack had worked on farms and had become deeply interested in dairy cattle. He went back to the city high school and tried vainly to get the faculty interested in agricultural subjects. When he had delivered a monologue in biology class which was both accurate and specific about artificial insemination of dairy cattle, he was promptly suspended from school. He never bothered to go back.

"All they cared about was football," he told me. "Couldn't get them interested in any higher subjects."

During his eighteen years, Jack had grown some powerful muscles. Before the morning was over, Dad was muttering that the boy must even have muscles inside of his head. He would climb up a ladder with a load of lumber that would have staggered an elephant and then nothing more would be heard from him for a time. Dad would scramble up and find Jack writing the names of all of the girls he had ever known on a rafter.

"Lookin' for me, Colonel?" he would ask in surprise.

Jack had his own names for tools and the carpentering processes. To him, a hammer was a mallet; all nails were tacks; a ruler was a measurer and all screws were bolts.

"Should I rip up this here piece of board?" Jack would ask, to determine whether Dad wanted him to use the saw.

"Must I bolt this in place?" he would ask, waving a screw driver around.

Half of the time, Dad wouldn't understand what the man

40

mountain was talking about and Jack would mutter to me: "Guess the Colonel ain't hearin' so good today."

Jack never dropped a tool when he finished using it, nor did he put it back in the tool box. He always stretched his arm straight up, stood on his toes and found some place eight feet from the ground where he would lay down a hammer, pencil or pliers. Dad would have to get a ladder when he wanted to recover a tool.

Through all of the years of Dad's building activities, I had studiously avoided learning any more about carpentering than was absolutely necessary. I did not want to compound the structural felonies he was committing constantly. But during that morning, I was able to learn a lot from watching this pair in action. By observing their methods, I could see how the job could have been done the right way.

Jack would help Dad as he measured and sawed a timber to make a rafter. When they tried to put it in place, they would find it was too short.

"I could see you was choppin' that one too short, Colonel," Jack would say.

"Why didn't you tell me, then?" Dad would roar.

"Just wanted to see the expression on your face when you found out," Jack would reply, and snicker.

The working party was ready for lunch early, so I told Connie that I would make some sandwiches for the men. When I informed Dad that I was knocking off to get lunch, Jack immediately stowed the tools away in the eaves and followed me into the house.

I put a loaf of bread, some butter and a block of cheese on the table and decided to get out Connie's grill and make toasted cheese sandwiches. There were a couple of loose screws on the grill and it took a few minutes for me to tighten them up. When I returned to the table with the grill, Jack asked:

"Whatcha fixin' to cook, Doc?"

"Toasted cheese sandwiches," I replied.

"I like 'em just as well not toasted," he said.

This was immediately apparent. The loaf of bread, the butter and most of the cheese had disappeared.

"Got any more bread?" he asked.

After lunch, I did my best to warn Connie about Jack's capacity for food. But there are some subjects which words are inadequate to describe and Jack's appetite was one of them. So, when the nine of us sat down to dinner that evening, there was enough food for ten people. Jack ate twice as much as anyone and then sat there looking hungry. Connie took care of this situation by giving him a loaf of bread and a jar of peanut butter which he, in turn, took care of.

The children observed this trencherman in action with un-mixed awe. Larry, at last, had found someone who could out-eat him. Claire, the little flirt, said:

"You must of dood some hard work today, Jack, for to get such a big appletite."

"Jack can eat more 'an th' hipmopopmus at th' zoo," Janie observed in her matter-of-fact way.

Jack's attitude toward the children was as changeable as spring weather. He would wrestle all five of them at once, take them swimming, play baseball with them and even get down on his hands and knees, with a length of two-by-six on his back, and let the little girls see-saw on him. But he always referred to them as a bunch of little brats and, whenever there seemed to be any danger that they would get the idea that he liked them, he would turn on them.

42

The girls hung around our construction project most of the time. They dragged Janie's countless dolls out to the lumber pile and used them in their incessant you-be-the-mama-I'll-be-the-papa game. Every time Jack would move any lumber off the pile, thus disarranging their playhouse, they would utter loud howls of protest. If they didn't get out of his way fast enough, Jack would pick a couple of them up, set them on the rafters and laugh at their shrieks.

During working hours, Jack maintained a disapproving attitude toward Larry. For Larry enjoyed an allergy to work, of any kind. His only interest in our progress was to note with dismay that the lumber pile did not spread over as wide an area as it had originally. It covered a good part of the front lawn which did not, therefore, have to be mowed. Jack kept needling me to put Larry to work on our job as an apprentice, but I didn't have much luck with this idea. Larry took to disappearing, along with some of our digging tools.

I spotted my son, finally, sneaking out toward a little patch of woods on the edge of the island. Jack and I crept up on the spot and found Larry, covered with sweat and dirt. He was standing in a deep hole which he evidently had been digging.

"What are you doing?" I demanded.

"Building a hiding place," he said blandly.

"Who're you hiding from?"

"You guys."

"Why?"

"So you can't make me do a lot of hard work."

But, for all of the Herculean efforts which went into construction, we did not progress very fast. As we approached the last week end of Dad's stay, the addition was still a good many hundred man hours away from completion. Dad said

43

that he absolutely had to get back to town on Sunday. In the face of this announcement, I persuaded him to restore the big double sink to its rightful place so that my bride would have that, at least, in which to bathe.

"What'll we do now?" I asked Dad desperately.

"Maybe some of the boys will be down this week end to give us a hand," he said. "There really isn't so much more to finish up."

The boys to whom he referred were members of a family which owned a cottage on the mainland. There were four brothers, countless cousins, uncles and friends connected with this family and if it was manpower Dad needed, he was looking in the right direction.

On Saturday, the sound of our hammers and saws attracted the attention of the gathering week-end crowd. Various representatives dropped in to see what we were up to now and, before they left, Dad signed each of them up for a day's work.

"Don't know whether we're going to have enough mallets and bolts to go 'round, Colonel," said Jack.

"Well, Jack," Dad said thoughtfully, "if Connie's been able to find enough food to keep you from getting emaciated these past couple of weeks, I think we'll be able to find enough tools."

"But you can't drive tacks with a jar of peanut butter," he replied.

On Sunday morning, we found ourselves surrounded by a sea of visiting helpers. They were a crowd of frustrated sidewalk superintendents. Within half an hour, there was more confusion than had been seen since the Tower of Babel project. Window frames were going in upside down. Shingles began to run in wavering, up-and-down courses. One doughty little band of helpers would be busy sawing a fourteen-foot piece

44

of two-by-four in half to get two seven-foot pieces. Another would be cleating two seven-foot pieces together to make the fourteen-foot length they needed.

Within half an hour, Dad was on the verge of raving madness. No one would pay any attention to him. Active direction of the construction had been taken over by two other people. One of them was our neighbor Dick, who decided that Dad didn't know what he was doing. He organized his own work party and went ahead. The other straw boss was Dick's uncle, a portly gentleman who stood well back from the house, puffing on a large cigar and shouting orders to which no one paid much heed.

Jack contributed to the confusion by explaining to anyone who asked what was to be done. Since his idea of what Dad had in mind was, at best, vague, it was no wonder that the wrong doors were being hung backwards in the wrong frames. Whenever Dad discovered a horrible mistake, Jack would fall down on the ground and roar with laughter.

At a time when the confusion had reached what I assumed was its maximum, a new helper arrived from across the creek. He took a quick look at the job, announced that everything done up to that time was wrong, and began to tear things down.

It wasn't safe to go near the place. I went back to stand on the lumber pile. Jack came along and picked up the boards I was standing on. If I hadn't jumped, he would have carried me off with the lumber and, for all I know, would have bolted me in place. The roof looked like the safest place to me, so I scrambled up the ladder. I had barely gotten off the top rung before someone snatched the ladder away and left me stranded.

From my perch on the roof, I spotted Connie, standing on

45

the edge of the crowd and watching the scene with obvious dismay. Her expression betrayed the fear that, if this kept up for another two hours, her family was not even going to have a roof over its head. The girls were clinging to her skirts, as if they were the daughters of a Georgia family watching as Sherman's Yankee troops sacked the family manse.

It was while I was sitting on the edge of the roof, feeling sorry for her, that Jack decided to put his mallet up there for safekeeping. It landed on my big toe and I concentrated on feeling sorry for myself. I saw Connie dart off and, a few minutes later, I heard our car start.

"Uh-oh," I muttered. "I bet she's headed back to New York to get a bath in a tub."

I was determined not to get down off that roof until order was restored. And a few minutes later I was relieved to hear Connie return in the car. I crept toward the edge of the roof to get a look at what was going on below. I was cautious as I peeked over, half expecting that Jack would pick that time and place to deposit a crow bar. Finally, I spotted Connie circulating through the crowd, oblivious to the danger that lay about her.

She approached the helpers one by one and then I saw them begin to drift away. It wasn't long before no one was left on the job but Dad, who just stood there shaking his head sadly. Jack finally reappeared and I yelled at him:

"Hey, bring the ladder over here so I can get down."

"Okay, Doc," he said, "I was lookin' for you. Thought maybe you was buried under a pile of boards."

"Where's everybody?" I asked suspiciously.

"Around t'other side of the house, in the shade," he replied. "Connie had a real compustible idea."

46

When I walked around the house, I could see that she had.

All of our helpers were gathered around a wash tub filled with ice and cans of beer. Connie was opening the beer and passing it around. Seeing this, I slipped back around the house and hid all the tools. From time to time, one of the volunteers would amble around the corner to see what was going on in the building line. Finding neither tools nor helpers, he would return to the tub of beer.

Within an hour, there was the sound of close harmony on the shady side of the house and I knew that the danger of any further work was past.

Chapter 6

O U R dream house, after weeks of struggling with it, still looked like something out of a nightmare. But we consoled ourselves with the knowledge that, somehow, our amalgamated family was getting along better than we had dared to hope.

During their first days in their new home, Cynthia and Claire received the guest treatment from my children. Nothing was too good for the new sisters and even Larry made only passing attempts to harass them.

Dad and Jack had no sooner gone back to town, leaving the uncompleted addition to the house, than the four girls moved their dolls into the unfinished rooms. Here they established a you-be-the-mama game on a large scale. Janie, the baby of my family, owned some two dozen dolls, all of which were named Tweenie except one. This was a Japanese house-boy doll, called Foo Young. From this supply of dolls, all four of the girls were able to draw substantial families. Pets for the participating families were furnished by Lynn, who had a passion for collecting animals, live or stuffed.

The girls would have one argument in the morning and one

48

in the afternoon over who would be the mama or who was to have Foo Young working for her family that day. At regular intervals, Larry would barge into the game to see what he could stir up. One day, he appeared after a great clanging of bells and shrieking of sirens to inform the girls that their houses were on fire and that he was the fire department. He had pretty well soaked down one room of the addition and three girls with the garden hose before I interceded. On other occasions, he would appear as an FBI man searching the place for stolen atomic secrets or he would be a radio announcer to interview the dolls for a man-on-the-street broadcast. Whatever his approach, it was designed to provoke the sort of uproar which twelve-year-old boys revel in.

Larry's most successful coup of this kind came off on the day when he staged the frame-up on Lynn's pet bear, Theodore. Lynn was a gentle, sensitive child and deeply religious. She did her best to behave as she had learned in Sunday School that a girl should behave. She applied her code of Christian ethics to her dealings with other humans—as well as animals. In return, she expected both people and animals to do likewise. She insisted, for instance, that Theodore the Bear must be a paragon of virtue, who would neither think of growling nor robbing a bee hive.

Theodore was an over-stuffed Teddy which I had bought for her once when, as a three-year-old, she had hurt herself. By now, he was a little frayed around the cuffs, but he was still her favorite. She took him to bed with her every night and told him all of her troubles.

After lunch one day, I strolled out to the addition to investigate an unusually noisy disturbance. I found Lynn shrieking at Larry, who in turn was pointing at Theodore and laughing uproariously.

"Theodore's been stealing honey," Larry shouted.

"Larry, you're mean," Lynn wailed in rage. "You know Theodore wouldn't do anything wrong."

I looked at the Teddy bear sprawled in the corner and there undoubtedly was a suspicious smear around his mouth. My eyes fell on the jar of honey in his arms. I looked quickly at it and then I turned on Larry. I could see Lynn's face brighten, but when she heard me speak her expression changed quickly.

"Hey," I roared at Larry. "Isn't that the jar of imported locust honey I've been saving?"

Then Lynn let out another wail.

"Oh, Daddy, you're awful. Poor Theodore's been taught to steal and all you care about is your old imported honey."

She went rushing into the house and I heard her call: "Mommy, mommy. . . ."

It was the first time I had heard any of my children call Connie "Mommy." They always used her first name, just as Claire and Cynthia called me "Al." We had told them that they could call us whatever they wanted and had been anxious not to force them into anything. Naturally, we hoped that eventually we would become "Mother" and "Daddy" to all of them. In fact, we winced a little when we heard the children speak among themselves of "my mother" or "your father." Lynn was now the first to turn to Connie as "Mommy" and she never called her anything else, after that.

But Cynthia and Claire were not, apparently, ready to accept me on this basis. They both regarded me with slight uneasiness, as if they were afraid that I was going to turn on them suddenly.

50

Cynthia lived in a more or less constant state of anxiety. Her glasses, somehow, seemed to magnify the solemn, worried look around her eyes. She was a child who always seemed to be having her little troubles. When she closed a door, the latch wouldn't catch and it would invariably open again. When she tied her shoe laces, she wouldn't get the knot tight and they would come untied. Each of these small mishaps caused her to utter a bitter protest against the fate she felt was plaguing her.

"Darn door," she would mutter, slamming it a second time so hard that the house would shake.

Or, she would say:

"Mommy, you've just got to get me some new shoe laces. These darn things just won't stay tied."

Confusion seemed to swirl around Cynthia like clouds around a mountain top. When she opened a book, she always discovered that it was (a) the wrong book or (b) upside down. When she put on a skirt, it would always be backwards. She would usually try to put her right foot in her left shoe.

The facet of Cynthia's personality which amused us most was the way she got jokes mixed up. One day, I repeated to Connie an old W. C. Fields' joke that seemed appropriate to something about which we had been talking.

"Fields was tending bar in a western saloon," I told Connie, "and one of the customers said to him: 'Hear you buried your wife.' And Fields looked at him solemnly and said: 'Had to. She died.'"

Later that day, I heard Cynthia talking to Lynn.

"Your daddy told my mommy the funniest joke today."

"What was it?" Lynn asked.

"Well, there was this funny man out West in a barn and

another man, I don't know who he was, said to the funny man: 'I hear your wife died.' And the funny man says: 'She had to. I buried her.'"

The greatest of all Cynthia's worries concerned her hair. She had lovely, soft blonde hair which grew out straight as a ruler. Her pretty little sister Claire had curly hair. Within five minutes after any stranger had been introduced to the two of them, there was sure to come the inquiry, addressed in honeyed tones to Claire: "Where did you get those pretty curls?"

Years of listening to this had left their mark on Cynthia. Of all things in the world, she wanted curly hair the most. But her hair seemed to have muscles and, as soon as Connie curled it, it would straighten out as if rigor mortis had set in.

Cynthia was a child who was hungry for affection. Whenever I gave her a hug or a kiss, she would glow like a lightning bug. But as much as she wanted love, she had never figured out exactly how to go about getting it.

Her little sister Claire was the direct opposite. While Cynthia buried her emotions deep, Claire's were on the surface. When she was angry, she had a temper tantrum. When she was happy, she bubbled. She was the personification of the little girl, who had a little curl. Claire was completely natural. If she liked a stranger who came to the house, she would jump on his lap immediately and put her arms around his neck. If she didn't like him, she would simply give me a baleful look. But Claire liked almost everyone and, in addition to being as pretty as a movie star, she was an outrageous little flirt.

Having Claire and Janie in the same family, it developed, was going to be like having a Shirley Temple and a Margaret O'Brien in the same movie. Formerly, moon-faced, even-featured little Janie had been the star performer in our family show. Janie was a few months older than Claire and as a pair of cuties, they were hard to beat. But, like any pair of cuties, they engaged in an incessant, undercover struggle to occupy the center of the stage. When I saw them maneuvering for this spot, I always thought of what had happened at the Christmas service in the Sunday school which they both attended in Florida.

The children had been decked out in little choir suits, with huge red bows under their chins. Claire and Janie, the smallest and prettiest children in the group, had been given a position in the middle of the stage, a step in front of the rest. The choir was arranged on a stage, behind a drawn curtain and, as the house lights dimmed, they began to sing "Hark, the Herald Angels Sing."

The curtain was still drawn as the pastor stepped on the stage and invited the audience to join in the next chorus.

"Our little angels will lead us in singing," he said beatifically.

He parted the curtains to reveal the little angels. All of them were lifting their faces toward heaven, save Claire and Janie. Each had decided that there was one single square foot of space in the exact center of the stage where she wanted to stand. Bows askew, they were pushing, pulling and batting each other over the head with their hymn books while the choir sang on.

But, like the older children, the little girls had been so full of *noblesse oblige* since we had settled down together on Dukehart Island that there had been no friction. Every evening, Connie and I congratulated ourselves and wondered how much longer it could last.

The era of good feeling came to an abrupt and noisy end one day, about a month after we had been married. Janie and Lynn, with Larry egging them on, fell into a purely inter-family quarrel with Cynthia and Claire. All of the resentments over sharing toys, sharing Mother's love and Daddy's favor and doing extra chores suddenly boiled over. The bickering went on for most of the day. Connie and I listened in dismay as her girls loudly bewailed the cruel fate that had caused them to leave their old home and my children angrily suggested that they both go back where they came from.

Dinner that evening was a strained affair, with Cynthia and Claire on one side of the table and Larry, Lynn and Janie on the other. Connie and I were squarely in the middle.

Before the meal was over, I found myself angry with my children. And Connie, trying to make up for my curtness, was smothering them with solicitous attention. While I was doing everything I could to make Cynthia and Claire feel really wanted in their new home, it seemed to me that Connie was treating them rather coolly.

The children forgot about their quarrel by morning and were back to normal. But the whole thing had left Connie and me a little shaken.

"It worries me," I said to her. "They were so intense about it."

"Maybe we're expecting too much," she said. "It's a hard adjustment for all of them."

As the days went by, I noticed that Connie would scold her girls whenever they got into an argument with mine—no matter whose fault it had been. I found myself angrily banishing Larry to his room whenever any unpleasantness started.

"It doesn't look as if we can ever make them into one family," I said in discouragement.

54

"Maybe it's partly our fault," Connie suggested.

"How could it be our fault?" I demanded. "They're the ones who aren't getting along together."

"I mean, maybe we're aggravating this two-family feeling by the way we treat them."

"I don't think I treat mine any differently from yours," I said defensively. "And you're just as good with mine, as if they were your own."

"But you do treat mine differently," she insisted.

"Why, I haven't punished either of them since they've been here. And I can't say that about my own," I replied heatedly.

"That's just it. You're tough with your kids, but you handle mine as if they were made of glass."

"You do the same thing."

"I know. I don't want them to call me a mean old step-mother."

"I suppose it does make things worse," I agreed. "Our own must resent the way we're so nice to the others. And so they act worse."

"I wish we could stop talking about 'my children' and 'your children,'" she said. "They're *our* children now."

"Okay," I agreed. "From now on, I'll be as tough with one as with another. We'll get some discipline around this place."

When I dropped my jolly Old Saint Nick approach toward Cynthia and Claire, I began to correct their behavior just as I did the others'. Whatever Cynthia thought about this change, I couldn't be sure because she kept it to herself. But whenever I got after Claire, she gave me a poisonous look and flounced out of the room.

I knew that we were heading for a showdown.

It came finally one morning when Claire returned from the store with a bar of candy.

"I wouldn't want you to eat that before lunch, little lady," I said.

" 'Kay," she said gaily.

Half an hour later, I found her munching on the candy bar. She looked at me guiltily.

"Didn't I tell you not to eat that?" I demanded.

"You're not the boss of me," she said firmly.

"I'm not, huh?" I roared.

"Mommeee . . ." she shrieked and took off as if she had, at last, come face to face with a real, live boogie man.

I caught her on the wing, intending to give her a stern talking-to. But she kicked me in the shins and that did it. I led her into her room, wailing like a banshee. There I turned her over my knee and administered the classic treatment.

"Now we'll see who's the boss of you," I said, as I stomped out.

Claire ran howling to her mother, but she got little consolation there and so she went back to her room to suffer alone.

The other children were bug-eyed with wonder and finally Larry sidled up to me and said:

"Attaboy, Pop. I was wondering how long you'd let those little brats get away with it."

"You better watch your own step, Junior," I said. "Once this sort of thing gets started, it might not stop with one."

"What did *I* do?" he demanded innocently.

"Nothing—yet," I said ominously.

Claire pouted during lunch and Cynthia kept eyeing me nervously. By now, I was feeling most uncomfortable and before the meal was over I was suffering from indigestion and remorse.

56

"I feel like a dog," I told Connie, as I prepared to go out and weed the garden after lunch.

"Well, you shouldn't," she said stoutly. "I don't believe in spanking, but if I did—I'd say that was the time she had one coming."

Just before dinner, I crept back into the house, cleaned up and sat down out on the porch to think things over. I was waiting for Connie to join me when Claire appeared.

"Mommy said this would make you feel better," she said, handing me a cool drink.

"Oh, thank you very much, dear."

She stood there for a minute, looking at me speculatively.

"I wonder did you shave your whiskers today?" she asked.

"Sure," I said. "Why?"

"I wanted to give you a kiss, for you're such a nice daddy."

She jumped into my lap, gave me a hug and a kiss and began to chatter happily. When Connie joined us a few minutes later, Claire was busy putting bobby pins in my hair.

"You two seem to be having a nice time," Connie observed.

"I'm fixin' Daddy's hair, for it will look all pretty and curly like mine," Claire said.

At dinner, Claire and I were the best of buddies again. But I noticed that Cynthia was still watching me anxiously. After we had left the table, I heard her talking to Lynn.

"I think that was mean of your father to spank Claire," she said.

"Boy!" said Lynn. "She was asking for it."

"Well, he better not spank me," Cynthia said defiantly.

"You better not kick him in the shins, or he'll do it. And he spanks hard."

"Humph," Cynthia said.

I reported the conversation to Connie a little later.

"So, I get back on good terms with one, and now the other's mad at me."

"We have our troubles, don't we?" she said.

"Do you think we'll ever make it into one family?" I asked.

The next day, we kept an ear cocked in the direction of the addition, where the girls were playing. We had been expecting another outbreak of violence between the two families. There was violence, finally, but it did not develop as we had expected.

Lynn and Cynthia came flouncing into the house, their arms loaded with stuffed animals.

"You little girls can just play by yourselves from now on," Lynn shouted back angrily.

"Yes," Cynthia added. "Go ahead and play with your old dolls. We've got Lynn's animals and some dolls of our own."

"What's the matter?" I asked.

"Daddy," said Cynthia. "You're liable to have to do some more spanking of those little brats."

I could hear Janie giggle.

"We don't care about those big brats, do we, Claire? We can have fun without 'em."

"'Kay," said Claire cheerfully. "You be the mama now."

From time to time, Lynn would shout some insult at the little girls and they would reply in kind.

"Well," I said to Connie, "this is a new twist—our kids fighting our kids."

"They're acting like one family now, *Daddy*," she said.

"What's all the racket?" Larry demanded finally. "Aren't you going to do anything about the way those brats are fighting?"

"Oh," I beamed, "that's okay. It's all in the family."

58

Chapter 7

 W HEN I settled on Dukehart with
my children, I had been seized with the urge to do something
with the two acres of more or less undefiled soil which we
owned. Like many another city man, long a prisoner of steel
and concrete, I wanted to dig my hands into the earth and see
what I could bring forth.

That first summer, I contented myself with planting a watermelon patch. I tended it with loving care and produced some
fine melons. During the second summer, I grew more ambi-
tious and planted a kitchen garden. Before the bugs and disease
to which vegetation is prey had managed to take over, the
garden had produced so much that I was afraid we were going
to be crowded off the place.

Practically the first thing I did upon my return from Florida,
in preparation for my marriage with Connie, was to plant a
garden. This was part of my plan to be the Hardy Pioneer. I
was out to beat the system. Not only would I do all the building and repairing on the house, but I would also grow my own
food. This was to be my answer to civilization.

My father had appeared one week end with a copy of a paper-bound, dollar book which was enjoying quite some popularity. It advanced the thesis that people should leave the cities, buy an acre of ground and raise most of their own food, thus becoming healthier, wealthier and wiser. The book, having proclaimed the idea that you could do a lot of living on a little land, went on to tell—chapter by chapter—how to establish this paradise. There were instructions on how to raise chickens, blueberries, turkeys, walnuts, pigs, sheep, fruit trees, rhubarb and rabbits. It all sounded as easy as going into debt, and a lot more fun.

The book was just what I was looking for. As soon as I had finished reading it, I seceded from the United States and adopted this whole new way of life, from Alfalfa to Zucchini. A day seldom went by that I didn't discuss with Connie my plan to establish a self-sufficient little homestead on Dukehart Island. But, since I talked about homesteading with the same enthusiasm that I discussed my plans for being a second Shakespeare, raising five perfect children and reforming the world, she didn't seem to take me too seriously.

Finally, I got her to read my book of instructions.

"What do you think of it?" I demanded.

"I just can't get that interested in food," she replied.

With no more encouragement than this, I went ahead with my dream. Dad and Jack, who came down every week end to work on the addition, were the only ones who shared my enthusiasm. Dad's life dream was to retire to Dukehart and carry out this sort of plan, himself. Jack was interested because edibles, even in the drawing-board stage of development, were close to his heart.

When Jack appeared one week end, he demanded:

"Bought any sheep yet?"

"Nope," I said and laughed.

"Thought we might be havin' lamb chops for dinner tonight."

When he saw Connie stagger home from the store with a load of milk for the week end, he said:

"My land—all that milk for this li'l ol' family? You ought to buy a cow."

"You ought to try drinking water when you're thirsty," Connie replied. "Then we wouldn't need so much milk."

"I drink water," Jack replied, "but it only makes me thirsty. Maybe I should just drink beer."

"Not my beer," I protested.

"Daddy's kind of beer is terrible," Janie observed.

"Why?" I demanded.

"All beer is," she replied.

"Well, you don't have to drink it. You stick to milk, young lady."

"Your daddy's going to get a cow and you can have all the milk you want," Jack said.

"Over my dead body," Connie replied. "I don't like cows."

"Aw, cows are beautiful," Jack protested. "Such soft eyes."

"I thought you loved all animals," I said.

"I love cows," Connie said firmly. "But I just don't want one around."

"Suppose we get goats?" I suggested. "Goats give milk."

"Camels give milk, too," she said. "More camels drink camels' milk than any other kind!"

"Goats don't eat as much as cows," I persisted. "We've got enough land to pasture a couple of goats."

"Have you ever tasted goats' milk?" she asked.

"No. But the book says it's just like cows' milk."

"I've always heard it has a strong taste."

"Depends entirely upon the way it's handled," I said learnedly, quoting from my book. "If you are careful with it, it tastes fine. It's naturally homogenized and much easier to digest than cows' milk. This is because the curd . . ."

"Well, I want to taste some before you buy any goats."

"I used to subscribe to a goat magazine," Jack said.

"I didn't know you were interested in goats," I said in surprise.

"I wasn't," he said. "Subscribin' to magazines used to be sort of a hobby."

"Well, reading's a good hobby," I said.

"Oh, I didn't read 'em. I just subscribed."

I looked at him incredulously.

"See!" he said, "nobody ever understands me."

"I'm doing my best to understand. But maybe you'd better go over this again slowly."

"I subscribed to magazines, because I like to get mail," Jack said. "Nobody ever wrote me letters, so I got magazines."

"I see," I said gravely.

"I liked to get mail because the postman was a pal of mine. When he came to the house with my magazines, we'd chew the fat. See?"

"Yes," I admitted. "And that's how you happened to subscribe to the goat magazine?"

"Sure. Magazines about goats and rabbits and chickens are cheaper than the big magazines. And I figured that if I should ever want to read a magazine, I wouldn't want to read about such a digustipatin' thing as people. Animals are much more interestin'."

"Mal de plume," I replied.

About this time, Dad came snorting along to find out why we weren't on the job.

"Go on and help him," Connie whispered, "before you hurt his feelings."

So I took my carpenter's apron down off the bridge lamp in the living room, where I hung it out of a habit of my bachelor days. We worked hard on the addition and on Sunday Dad and I uncrated the bathtub. We turned it over on Jack's back and he crept into the house like a turtle. Connie squealed with delight when she saw the tub.

"Of course, you won't be able to use it for a while," Dad cautioned, explaining that there was still a lot of plumbing to be done and that we were going to have to dig a new septic tank.

"I've got to get Connie out of the sink," I said in dismay. "Every time she takes a bath, I have to spend half an hour picking steel wool out of her bottom with a pair of tweezers."

"She ought to take showers like the rest of us," Dad observed.

"But she's not like the rest of us," I observed.

"Maybe I should keep Jack down here to help dig the septic tank," I said. "Unless he'd miss the postman too much."

"Nope. I reckon I could stay for a spell," Jack said.

And so it was agreed that Jack's daily wage would be charged against my account with Dad. Early the next morning, we set out to dig a hole in the ground, six feet deep and six feet on all sides.

"What's that phobia Connie's got so she can't go in the shower bath?" Jack asked.

"Claustrophobia—fear of close places," I said.

"That's a good word. Gotta add that to my vocab'lary. I'll surprise Mrs. T. with it when I go home."

63

"Mrs. T.? Who's she?"

"Me mother. You shoulda heard me when I went home last week and used some of those big words I learned from you."

We dug for a time and then Jack said:

"Hope I don't catch that closetphobia down in this hole."

"It's not contagious," I assured him.

"I dunno. Every time I sit down to the table now, I feel all crowded and squigged up."

"You're not crowded. Your stomach is just getting so big you can't get near the table. By the time we've dug down six feet, we'll both be so skinny we can fit in here without feeling close."

At the end of the day, I came dragging in the house, covered with dirt and sweat.

"A fine honeymoon," I protested to Connie.

"You shouldn't do all this for me," Connie said solicitously. "I really don't mind it in the sink."

But we kept on digging for a couple of days. Then, one morning after breakfast, Jack announced:

"I ain't in a diggin' mood today."

"What do you mean?" I demanded.

"Well, it's just that some days I feel like diggin' and some days I feel like doin' somethin' different. I'm out of my diggin' mood."

"So what kind of mood are you in?" I asked gently.

"A carpenteering mood. Too bad the Colonel ain't here, or we could finish the house."

"Well," I said, "let's go see what we can find to carpenteer."

The morning air was filled, before long, with the sound of hammer and saw. When we came back in for lunch, Connie looked pleased.

"Trying to speed up Dad's little job?" she asked.

"I wouldn't dare touch his job," I replied.

She looked dismayed.

"What was all the hammering, then?"

"We've started building a barn," I said proudly.

She shot me a look of genuine dismay.

"A barn?"

"Yeah, we've got to have some place to keep the goats."

"Goats?"

"Sure, didn't we decide to get goats instead of a cow?"

"Did we?" she demanded.

"Sure," I laughed. "So we need a barn."

"Imdudiously," Jack said.

It happened that I had to go to Washington the following week. From one of Jack's goat magazines I got the address of a place outside of town where goats were kept and I visited the establishment. The goats I was introduced to were Toggenburgs and it was love at first sight. The Toggenburg goat is one of the four or five breeds which have been imported to this country from other parts of the world, where goats' milk is more widely used than cows' milk. These goats are brown, with uniform white markings on the face, tail and feet. The ones I saw were beautiful, alert friendly animals.

The lady who owned the herd told me something about them. They had no strong odor, as I could tell, and were extremely clean in their habits. They wouldn't touch food, once it had dropped on the ground, and under no circumstances would eat a tin can or red flannels. One cow, my hostess said, would eat as much as six goats and wouldn't produce as much milk. She had goats that gave seven quarts of milk a day, she said.

65

I went home, sold on milk goats, and carrying a sample quart of milk. The lady had charged me fifty cents for it, after explaining that she usually got seventy-five cents a quart.

"Just put it in glasses on the table," I told Connie. "I bet the children never notice the difference."

I was wrong about that, for they all commented on the odd taste.

"I thought it tasted funny, too," Connie told me.

"Well, I didn't," I insisted.

"You're not still thinking of getting goats?" she said.

"Just because they didn't like the milk? I'm not going to raise such fussy kids. They'll get used to it."

"Aw," she said sympathetically. "That's mean."

After this, I was afraid to tell Connie that I had already paid for two goats. So Jack and I worked away on the barn, when we had time, and finally got it in shape for its occupants. One day, I made some excuse for Jack and me to go to town. I hid the back seat of the Ford in the bushes and we headed for the goat farm suitably prepared.

When we got there, the goats jumped contentedly into the back of the car and we started home. As long as the car was moving, the goats kept quiet and I had almost forgotten we had them aboard as we headed into downtown Washington traffic. Then I began to notice people doing quick double-takes when they saw our car. When we had to stop in traffic, the goats would get restless and noisy. Before long, our car was attracting more attention than a circus parade.

I burrowed down behind the wheel and fervently hoped that I wouldn't encounter any bank presidents from whom I might want to borrow money some day. But Jack was delighted at the attention. We would pull up alongside a car at a

66

traffic light and Jack would roll down a back window, push one of the goat's heads out and roar with delight when the people in the next car looked up. I had to make him stop pinching the goats so they would go "Maaaa" as we passed a traffic cop.

We finally got free of city traffic and I hurried to get home before dark.

"I don't know how Connie's going to take this," I kept muttering.

We were about half way home, on a lonely stretch of road, when the car sputtered to a stop. We had run out of gasoline. Jack volunteered to walk down the road to a service station we could see. But when he got out of the car, the goats decided they wanted to get on the front seat. I couldn't control both of them and so it was decided that we would just have to walk them down to the service station.

Jack stepped along proudly with his goat and when an automobile came along behind us, he started waving it down wildly. The car slowed down, but then the driver took a horrified look at the goats and sped away as if he had seen a two-headed monster.

The goats insisted on stopping to graze, from time to time, but we finally made it to the service station. A couple of attendants burst out, rags in hand, ready to check the oil and wipe our windshields. When they saw the goats, they stopped dead in their tracks.

"We need some gas," I said quickly.

"Thought you fed them things tin cans," one of the attendants said.

Now that I was a goat owner, I couldn't see the humor of this remark.

"The car's just down the road—could you run one of us down with a can of gas?" I asked.

"You got a *car?*" the attendant demanded. "I thought maybe them billy goats was pullin' you in a cart."

"They're not billy goats," Jack said.

We finally got under way again and by now I was really worried. I estimated that we were going to be about as welcome at home as a two-week rain and I tried to get some reassurance from Jack on this point.

"Mammy's goin' to be right mad, I reckon," he said. "Bein' as we're late for dinner, in addition to totin' in a couple of strange goats."

When we pulled into the yard, Connie and the children burst out to greet us. Connie advanced toward the goats slowly and I watched her face closely.

"Oh, they're beautiful," she said rapturously.

Jack looked at me in bewilderment and I heaved a huge sigh of relief.

One of the goats, I told Connie, was already registered under the name Phyllis. Connie decided on the spot that the other should be named Prudence because she was so prim and dainty.

"What are those things hanging down?" Claire demanded.

"That's the udder, dear," Connie said.

"What a gutter for?" Claire insisted.

"That's where the milk comes from."

"How does it work?" she asked.

"Daddy'll show you," Connie snickered.

"Not me," I said. "I don't know how to milk the things. Besides, they won't give milk until they've had their kids."

68

"Are they going to have kids?" Connie asked. "Do you know how to handle that?"

"What's there to do?" I demanded.

"They might need help," she said. "Then what'll you do?"

She appeared to be so disturbed about the welfare of the goats that I said:

"I'll buy a book about goats, then."

"Maybe you better get the goats a book about people," Jack suggested, as he saw Connie lean over and tenderly brush Prudence's coat. " 'Specially women."

Chapter 8

O U R family was now firmly divided, or rather united, along lines which the children had worked out quite naturally for themselves. Larry was established as the young bull of the herd. Then there were the Big Girls— my Lynn and Connie's Cynthia—and the little girls, Janie and Claire. These twosomes played together, shared secrets, took their baths together and went to bed together. By and large, the step-sisters seemed to get along together better than the real sisters.

All of the girls called Connie "Mommy" now and all of them called me "Daddy." This, too, was something they had fallen into naturally. Larry still called Connie by her first name, but this was a recognition of the reality of their relationship. They were not so much like mother and son as like sister and young brother.

The little girls reminded me always of Tweedledee and Tweedledum. If Claire had one idea, Janie usually found it necessary to take another view, contrariwise. They were prin-

70

cesses from different kingdoms and neither would bow to the other. They got along together beautifully so long as everything between them was exactly even.

One day, I heard them agree to play a game of Cinderella. There was a long debate over which was to be the step-mother and which was to be Cinderella. I lost track of the situation until later when I heard Janie playing the part of the step-mother:

"All right, now, Cinderella. You've got to do hard work."

"But all I know how to do is to make fudge and jam some bread," Claire piped.

A few minutes later, they had reversed their roles and Janie was playing the star part. It was by such elaborate stratagems as this that they managed to get along.

The Big Girls had no such problem. Cynthia attached herself to Lynn like a little red caboose. Cynthia was sort of a chameleon, who changed her personality to suit the situation of the moment. She had been speaking with a southern accent two days after arriving in Florida. Now if she came wanting to have her hair braided, we would know that she found a new friend with braids.

Cynthia worshiped Lynn and where her idol went, there she went. If Lynn settled down to read, Cynthia read also. If Lynn closed her book and left the room, Cynthia followed. What Lynn liked, Cynthia ate. The ultimate came one day I saw Lynn stub her toe. Cynthia began jumping on one foot and moaning. Lynn, who was sitting on and rubbing the injured toe, looked at Cynthia suddenly asked:

"What's the matter, Cynthia?"

"I don't know," Cynthia replied with surprise. Then sud-

71

denly she remembered and said: "You stubbed your toe, didn't you?"

"Yeah, but you're hopping on the wrong foot."

"Oh," said Cynthia, and began hopping on the other foot.

Connie and I felt that if Cynthia needed someone as her heroine, she could have made a worse choice than Lynn. For Lynn was one of those rare children who turn out to be just about everything a parent could desire. She was now at an age where she was a child part of the time, and a young woman part of the time. When she was in the mood to be a child, she found Cynthia's unceasing imitation flattering. But when her grown-up spells hit her, she would complain to us that Cynthia was shadowing her. Then Cynthia would get a forlorn expression on her face and go off to see what the little girls were playing.

Lynn had always been a willing stooge for Larry. She had never shown any tendency to fight back when he pushed her around, which he did most of the time. We were curious to see what would happen now that she had a new status in the family, as Cynthia's White Goddess and arbiter of the little girls' disputes. On the Fourth of July we began to get an idea of what was in store for Larry.

This was to be our first formal holiday as a family and I wanted to make something of it. Jack, noting that everyone in town was going to the country for the holiday, announced that he thought he would go to town. I hoped that his departure would free me of my Hardy Pioneer role for a day.

But then Dad showed up, was disappointed to find Jack gone and said I would just have to help him rig up the drain pipe for the bathtub. He gathered together some old pieces of

72

brass bed posts, rubber hose, bailing wire and a random selection of second-hand plumbing fittings. By using such materials, Dad not only saved money, but he had the pleasure of repairing things when they broke down, which they always did.

This Fourth of July, our house was something of an ammunition dump. One of Larry's relatives, never a man to do things by halves, had sent down a supply of fireworks that would have sufficed for a municipal celebration in a town the size of Massilon, Ohio.

Larry had greeted the dawn with a salvo that must have been heard in Washington. He had kept up a steady drum fire since. Occasionally, there would come a loud shriek from one of the girls, followed by a short but intense burst of fire. This would indicate that Larry had succeeded in isolating one of them. Naturally, this was the sort of activity I wanted to get in on—or at least, under control.

Dad and I were just preparing to set foot out of the house to begin the plumbing job when Cynthia came streaking into the living room. Larry, loaded with high explosives, was pursuing her like a kamikaze pilot. In her flight, Cynthia knocked over a floor lamp. As it teetered, there were a couple of short explosions set off by Larry. Then came the crash of broken glass as the lamp smashed against one of the living-room windows.

Dad put down his plumbing tools without a word and turned to survey the damage. His lips were set in a tight line and I could see that he wasn't going to take this well, at all.

"No use trying to build anything new around here," he muttered. "Takes all my time to repair what gets broken."

"I'll fix that, Dad. Don't bother about it."

"No, I better do it myself," he said, looking speculatively at the window. "That window looks crooked, anyway. Should be straightened."

Replacing a small pane of glass in a window didn't look like a two-man job, so I wandered off to see whether I couldn't get our Fourth of July on a safer and saner basis. When I caught up with Larry, I disarmed him and we sat down for a quiet talk. I persuaded him that, instead of dissipating his fireworks on stray shots at his sisters, he should save them and stage a monster Independence Day Celebration.

"Get the whole family together," I said with enthusiasm. "Invite the neighbors. Serve lemonade and then shoot off all your fireworks. We'll have a big time."

"Okay. And I'll be the main speaker for the day."

"All right. And let the girls do something on your program, too."

"What can they do?" he demanded scornfully.

"Oh, you can think of something. Cynthia can do a handstand."

As a matter of fact, Cynthia spent so much time standing on her hands that, from day to day, I almost forgot what her face looked like. No matter where she was, she would suddenly do a cart wheel and begin walking around the room on her hands.

When Larry asked Lynn and Cynthia what they wanted to do, they fell into a lively discussion.

"Lynn, I think we should be confederates."

"What's a confederate, Cynthia?"

"You know—like in that movie we saw. Crooks who make phony money."

"What's that got to do with the Fourth of July?" Lynn demanded.

74

"Okay. Then I'll be an acrobat and do handstands. What'll you do?"

"You be the Statue of Liberty, Lynn," Larry suggested.

But when it came to fitting the little girls into the program, Larry was faced with a problem. Whatever part he suggested, they both wanted. No doubt, they were remembering the carol singing in the Florida Sunday school and wanted to make sure, in advance, that the other would not have the center of the stage. There was a long and bitter argument, but finally it died away and I concluded that Larry had found a solution.

A few minutes later, Claire and Janie came charging around the house, shouting happily. Both were attired in cowboy outfits and they were brandishing a pair of Larry's cap pistols.

"Oh, Daddy," Janie shouted. "This is goin' to be funner 'an anythin'."

"Swell. What are you going to be?"

"We're cowboys," Claire said.

"Cowgirls," Old Contrariwise corrected.

"We're Roy Rogers' wife," said Claire.

"Both of you?" I asked.

"Yeah," said Janie. "I'm Dale."

"And I'm Evans," Claire explained. "Now stick 'em up."

"No, Claire, we don't say stick 'em up. Our husbun does all 'at. We jes stay home and cook his tea."

"And his oakmeal, Janie. 'Tend he likes oakmeal gooder than anythin' else."

I leaned down and chucked Claire under the chin.

"You look cute," I said.

"Oh, not too," she replied demurely.

"How do you like my upsweet hairdo, Daddy?" asked Janie.

"Cute," I admitted, as they went chasing off.

Now that the Fourth of July celebration was back on the tracks, I decided I had better see how Dad was getting along with repairing the broken window pane. I discovered that he had taken the entire window out of its frame. He had cut a small piece of glass to replace that which was broken, but he was having trouble fitting the glass into place.

"What's the matter?" I asked. "Didn't you cut the glass straight?"

"Yes, it's straight. But the window seems to be warped. A square piece of glass won't fit it."

"Then why don't you cut the glass crooked to fit the window?"

"No. I better straighten up the window."

I watched as he forced the window back so it was square, but when he tried to replace it in the frame, it wouldn't fit.

"Guess I'll have to take that frame out and straighten it," he said.

"I still think it would have been easier to cut the glass crooked." I said, and walked off.

I was standing out in the yard sometime later, watching the kids get ready for the celebration. Lynn was doing all the hard work of moving chairs, while Larry stood by and directed her. I shook my head in wonder that she would take all this from him. I was still wondering when Connie appeared.

"What in the world is Dad doing?" she asked.

"The kids broke a pane of glass," I said. "He's putting in a new one."

"He's got half of the front of the house torn out," she said in alarm. "I'm afraid he'll go back to town and leave it like that."

I rushed around the house and found that Connie's report

was quite accurate. The window with the broken pane, two windows which flanked this, the frame which held them and a good bit of the siding from the front of the house had been removed.

"What's the matter?" I asked. "Termites?"

"Well, the window was warped. And then I found the frame was crooked. I straightened that out, but then the siding looked crooked. Now I guess the floor is off level. Think I'll have to get under there and jack up this side of the house a trifle."

The house had no basement and whenever it began to sag, Dad would go under with a tool that looked something like an automobile jack and raise it an inch or two. He could do this by himself, so I went back to check on Larry's progress.

The island was plastered with red, white and blue posters announcing the big event. Tickets had been passed out to all the neighbors. The girls had been rehearsed in their parts and Larry was hoarse from shouting at them. Lynn looked as if she was at last getting tired of being bossed around, and I was glad.

Just as the program was about to start, I rushed over to the house to tell Dad. But he was under the porch, jacking up the front of the house and said he wouldn't be able to come out just then. I went in the house and I could tell that he had made considerable progress in lifting the house. The living-room floor was now at such an angle that some of Larry's marbles, which had been on a book shelf, had rolled all the way to the other side of the room. I shouted this information under the house to Dad and he allowed that he would just have to jack up the middle of the house to match.

Then I took my seat for the show. Larry had rigged up a toy microphone on the speaker's rostrum and was giving an

77

annoyingly accurate imitation of his favorite disc jockey. Several neighboring adults had joined the audience. The program opened with Roy Rogers' wife, Dale and Evans, charging in on broomstick horses, firing their cap pistols. Then came Cynthia, walking on her hands, followed by stately, blonde Lynn. The latter was dressed, by special permission, in one of Connie's negligees and, as Miss Liberty, was carrying aloft a burning sparkler.

Larry sounded a fanfare on his bugle and then the children sang all the patriotic songs they knew. There came a point in the program where Cynthia arose to tell a joke.

"Why," she asked, looking at us wide-eyed through her glasses, "does the President wear red, white and blue pants?"

Everyone looked properly baffled by this query.

"To keep his expenders down," she said triumphantly.

"Ho, ho, ho, that's even funnier than if she'd told it right," boomed our jovial master of ceremonies. "But so much for the light side of our program. We will now have a reading of the preamble to the Constitution and of the Declaration of Independence by our guest speaker of the day, Mr. Lawrence S. Toombs."

He laid out copies of the documents from which he was going to read. Everyone in the audience smiled kindly as he waded through the first paragraphs, thinking no doubt how clever it was for a boy of that age to be able to read such big words without faltering. From time to time, Larry would pause to gulp water and would wave his glass at Lynn, imperiously demanding a refill. I wondered at her patience as she jumped up time after time to run to the pump.

Our boy orator was growing very hoarse by this time and

Roy Rogers' wives were getting restless under the barrage of unintelligible words. They began to giggle and he shouted louder. This made the rest of the audience giggle, also. Then we began to guffaw at the sight of the red-faced, hoarse boy gulping water, gesticulating wildly and proclaiming that all men had certain inalienable rights. He merely swigged more water, got redder in the face and shouted louder.

The quantities of water he was pouring down his throat and shirt front were truly incredible. When, for perhaps the eighth time in the course of fifteen minutes, he sent Lynn after another glass of water, I noticed that she made a detour into the house on her way back from the pump. The glass of water she handed him looked a little cloudy, but he was too intent upon his peroration to notice this. A moment later, he took a huge gulp out of the glass and erupted like Vesuvius. I leaned over toward Lynn and asked:

"What did you put in the water?"

"Red pepper and dry mustard," she said.

"I'm surprised at you," I said mockingly.

"It's the Fourth, isn't it?" she giggled. "Well, that's my declaration of independence from that big, noisy slave driver. I've got some of those alien rights he's raving about, too."

Larry hopped around on the podium like a wild Indian as the audience roared. He was incapable of any sound other than an occasional whoop. Finally, just as he seemed to be on the verge of recovering the use of his voice, Lynn lit a sparkler and began to dance around him. The sparkler slipped out of her hand and landed in one of the boxes of fireworks which Larry had set aside for his display.

A few seconds later, there came a series of short explosions

79

and we retired to a safe distance. It was noisy while it lasted and those fireworks which did not explode prematurely were set off in short order by Larry.

At last, quiet descended on the island. Lynn had vanished and Larry, unable to talk above a whisper, was searching grimly for her. We interrupted him in his search for his runaway slave long enough to thank him for the fine, old-fashioned Fourth.

When I walked back to the house, I found Dad still at work. He had now allowed the floor to settle back to its original slant and was looking over the wreckage. With three windows and a good bit of the siding missing, the house looked like a child with two front teeth out.

"Well, that's too much of a job to finish today," he told me wearily.

"You're not going back to town and leave it like that?" I demanded.

"Nothing else I can do," he replied.

In dismay, I recalled the time, a couple of years before, when he had torn half of one side of the house out to install a fireplace. I had lived for two weeks with birds chasing insects through the house.

"Wait a minute," I said. "Connie will kill us if we don't get this put back together. I'll help you."

We worked until after dark and finally got the windows back in. It all looked just as crooked as it had when he had started that morning. Dad went off to get dressed for his trip back to town and I was relaxing on the porch when Larry approached.

"I saved one sky rocket," he said in a hoarse whisper. "All right if I set it off now?"

"I guess so," I said resignedly.

This had to be a production number, also, so Larry assembled all the girls and touched a match to his rocket.

The sky rocket started up in a spectacular climb, but when it got about half as high as it should have gone, it took a sudden turn and headed down. Sparks flying, the rocket headed straight toward the house. We ducked for cover as we heard a swoosh overhead and, before we could look up, we heard the tinkle of broken glass. The rocket had broken another window.

Dad, dressed for town and carrying his suitcase, appeared at this moment.

"Got any more glass?" I asked nervously. "I'll fix this one."

"Oh, what's the use?" he growled, as he stomped toward his car. "There'll just be another Fourth of July next year."

Chapter 9

IT wasn't long before Connie and I decided that two cooks were just the right number to spoil the broth.

We were both accustomed to running our own households. I was quite willing to retire undefeated from housekeeping after I married her. But no one, who didn't know this house we lived in, could have walked in and started keeping it without help. And, besides, Connie kept quoting back to me an interview I had given once in a moment of weakness. In it, I had said that the husband ought to help with the cooking and the chores around the house.

So, we both tried to run the place simultaneously. Then it was that some technical difficulties began to arise. For example, her idea of a nice lunch was a fruit salad, with a plate of fancy crackers and some cream cheese and olive spread. These items I considered to be beyond the means of a Pioneer Family and they left me hungry. I got more mileage out of bologna, peanut butter and store bread. When Connie cooked fish, she broiled it. When I cooked fish, I fried it and there was never enough lard in the house for me. She preferred prepared biscuit mixes and bought her cakes at the store. I rolled my own biscuits and baked my own cakes. When I wanted cornmeal to make the muffins we liked, all I would be able to find in the pantry would be the whole-wheat flour she preferred in muffins.

Since we were still honeymooners, we met these crises with nothing more violent than sad little sighs. But both of us could feel a situation building up.

One day, after I had clucked disapprovingly when I found Connie making a pudding with fresh milk instead of canned milk, she cocked her head and said:

"There are two kinds of people in the world. Those who squeeze the tooth-paste tube from the middle and those who squeeze it from the end."

"I squeeze it from the end," I said righteously.

"Let's face it," she said, and smiled. "I squeeze it from the middle."

"So?"

"So, you're going to do things your way and I'm going to do things my way and we can't change each other. And maybe we'd better stop trying to cook dinner together."

Finally, we agreed that I would cook breakfast for everyone every day, since it was a meal that Connie detested. In addition, I would cook one of my specialties for dinner once or twice a week. After that, I stayed out of her hair in the kitchen. Except that I still tried to convince her that my pressure cooker was a useful utensil and not, as she insisted, a lethal weapon.

Connie wanted every dinner to be a happy, chatty affair. She would never break into a pleasant conversation to tell the children not to eat peas with their fingers. Nor did she ever seem to notice that when she served something the children didn't want, they would push it to one side of the plate, cover it with a knife and fork and forget to eat it.

I was no man to let a little idle conversation stand in the way of discipline. The minute I spotted an elbow on the table or missed hearing a "please," I growled. I enforced on my new daughters the rule with which I had bludgeoned my children into eating their vegetables: no dessert unless your plate is clean. Gentle Connie winced when I barked and happy talk around the table fell off considerably.

Everyone began to gang up on me. I discovered that the children were stuffing food that they didn't like in their pockets, excusing themselves from the tables and flushing it down the bathroom drain. So I made them stay at the table until the meal was over. Then I noticed that Connie wouldn't serve the sort of things the children didn't like.

"Why don't we ever have that eggplant dish I like so much?" I asked her one day.

"The children won't eat eggplant," she said.

"We can't have eggplant any more because they won't eat it?" I demanded.

"Well, I didn't say that. But I don't like to force them. And anyway it doesn't have many vitamins in it."

"Well, I like it. Vitamins or not."

So, we had eggplant. I gave each child a respectable serving and closed my ears to their moans. To cover up my own discomfort, I provided plenty of happy chatter during the meal. When I had finished a third helping, I triumphantly called Connie's attention to the fact that the eggplant had disappeared from everyone's plate. For some reason, no one jumped up to take his plate off the table until we had finished our dessert.

Then, when I saw the kids clear the table, my chuckle of victory turned to a gurgle. The girls had all succeeded in hiding their eggplant under their plates where I couldn't see it. Larry admitted that he'd fed his to Tonker, under the table.

"I don't really think that this is the way to do it," Connie said after dinner.

"Well, I'll admit that it's not getting results," I said. "But what shall we do?"

"I think they'll learn good manners by example," she said. "And if we could explain to them why it's good to eat a balanced diet, I think they'd do it without being nagged."

I agreed to give her system a try. I didn't see any immediate improvement in manners. But conversation began to pick up, now that I was giving it a chance, and somehow I didn't seem to have indigestion after the meal was over.

We spent a lot of time explaining to the children the values of different kinds of food. They found the subject interesting. Once the girls decided that eating green vegetables and drinking milk was the *good* thing to do, they fell to with enthusiasm. We let them serve themselves and soon they were taking larger helpings of vegetables than we had ever dared dish out to them.

They were especially delighted when they learned that egg plant had a low vitamin content and that it wasn't necessary to eat it in order to stay healthy. One or two of them even ate some, after that.

One night, after the table had been cleared, Claire and Janie rushed into the kitchen and got down two glasses.

"Low the milk down from the 'frigrator for us, please Mommy," Janie demanded.

"You girls must be thirsty," Connie suggested.

"Nope, but I jes' amembered 'at I hardly drank a cent's worth of milk at dinner," Janie explained.

"An' I only drank a spoodle of it," Claire said.

They gulped down the milk.

"Come on, Claire," said Janie. "Now we don't have to werry about our fightamints."

"Feel my muskle," Claire said as they raced off.

I finally had to admit that Connie's plan had put over the idea with the children. We were driving down the road one day, when we passed a midget automobile. Janie said suddenly:

"Look, Claire. There goes a little car 'at didn't eat its vegetables."

But Connie and I were unable to find any such happy solution for our differences about the family finances. Our money woes could be summed up very simply. I couldn't be bothered too much about earning money and she couldn't be bothered about saving money.

I was devoting most of my energies to building the homestead, on the theory that once we had our own food supply, we wouldn't need much money. So, while I did my writing chores, my heart was in homesteading. And although Connie said that she could be just as happy without money, as long as we happened to have some on hand, it seemed to her that we should spend it. With a few dollars in her pocket, Connie was the greatest little one-woman spending spree in the country.

"You've done more to stimulate business in this part of the country than anything since Pearl Harbor," I told her one day.

But neither my piety nor my wit made any impression upon her. As long as we had it, she was bent on getting rid of it. Finally, I beat on the table and proclaimed an economy wave.

"All right," she said. "I'll make a list of everything I spend this entire week."

At the end of the week, she came in proudly with her list to report to me.

"How much did you manage to save?" I asked.

"Oh, I spent two dollars more than last week. But I kept a list of every cent of it."

I looked the list over quickly and I could see where one of the two dollars had gone. Half way down, there was the following item: "Budget book, to keep list of money spent—$1."

"The idea, apple dumpling, is not merely to keep a list. It's to spend less," I explained.

"But how can I spend any less?" she protested. "You can see everything on the list, there."

That's as far as I got with the economy wave. If I complained about expenses, Connie would produce her list and show me where it was all going. All I ever really found out was that she wasn't losing any money on the horses.

One day, she came in with excitement in her eyes.

"I've decided I won't spend *any* money at all," she said.

"Wonderful!" I exclaimed. "But tell me, angel, how are you going to buy the little odds and ends that we need—like clothes and groceries?"

"I'll just charge things at the store," she said triumphantly.

"But you're not going to spend any money?"

"How could I? I wouldn't even handle the money. You can just go down and pay the bill every week. Then you'll be sure I'm not wasting a cent."

"No," I said, looking at her thoughtfully. "You're doing fine this way. You just keep on making out your list."

As part of my plan to save money by living off the land,

I went to the store one day and invested a few dollars in Mason jars. I brought in a basket of tomatoes, set them down next to the jars and informed my bride that we were about to put up some tomatoes.

"Oh," she said in her smallest voice.

We spent most of the day canning five quarts of tomatoes.

"Aren't they beautiful?" I demanded when the steaming hot job was done. "Aren't you excited?"

"Well," said Connie, "you've spent heaven knows how much on jars and two of us have been working most of the day. Frankly, all I can see is about fifty cents' worth of canned tomatoes that I could have bought at the store."

"But they're ours—we didn't have to buy them," I said.

"What about the jars?"

"That's an investment. We can use them again."

"You mean you want to do this again?" she asked, mopping her forehead with the back of her hand.

"Sure. Next year, I'll plant enough vegetables so we can put up our whole year's supply."

"Oh dear," she said, putting her arms around me and burying her face in my shoulder.

"What's the matter?" I asked in alarm.

"I'm just not used to it. I mean, all this work and living this way."

"Oh, I'm sorry," I said sympathetically.

"It's all right. I'll get used to it. If it's what you want and you're sure, I'll learn to do it."

"It won't be so hard, after you get the hang of it," I assured her.

A couple of days later, Connie came and sat on the arm of my chair after dinner. She started to play with my hair and

I looked up at her. She had put on a new face and smelled of Chanel's best.

"I bet you're glad I'm not the kind of wife who's always wanting a fur coat or new diamonds," she said.

"It's just as well," I replied. "Because I haven't got enough dough to spend on them."

"But I could use my own money and be extravagant, couldn't I?"

"Sure, I suppose so. It's your money and you can spend it on anything you like."

"Do you mean it?"

"Why of course. What's on your mind, anyway?"

"I want to buy a deep freezer," she said suddenly.

"A deep freezer?"

"Yes. Then I won't have to do all that canning."

"But we can't afford . . . I mean that's the sort of thing I . . ."

But I could see that she had me mousetrapped.

"You said you didn't care what I spent my own money on," she said. "And I want a freezer."

She produced an advertisement for a ten-cubic-foot home freezer.

"And you get $100 worth of frozen food with it—free!" she exclaimed.

"Okay, we'll look into it next time we go to town."

"Why don't I just send them a check?" she said. "I've got it all made out."

I looked at her with disbelief.

"This isn't a bag of peanuts, dear. This will cost nearly four hundred dollars."

"It's a reliable store that's selling it, isn't it?"

89

"Sure."

"Well, what could I tell about a freezer by looking at it? It's just a big hunk of machinery to me. I'm going to mail the check tomorrow."

The freezer was delivered to the island a short time later. The store promised to notify us when our free food would be available. Connie was eager to try out the freezing process, so we put some wild blackberries, applesauce, surplus garden vegetables and a few non-productive hens down. These things barely covered the bottom of the big unit.

Dad picked up our free food in town a few weeks later. He brought it down one hot evening and we worked frantically to get it stored away. But we filled the freezer to the top and discovered that we still had about twenty-five dollars' worth of small steaks and frying chickens left over. Hastily, we packed an old electric refrigerator that stood on our porch, but still we had packages of food left over. We crammed the rest into our new refrigerator and for days we gorged on frozen delicacies so that they would not spoil.

"It's just like money in the bank," I said, patting the big freezer full of food affectionately.

"Speaking of money in the bank," Connie said. "I haven't any left. Have you?"

It appeared that the editors with whom I was dealing had also decided that my heart was in homesteading—and not in writing—and so I had been collecting more rejection slips than bank-deposit slips.

"Nope," I said casually. "But if we can get by until the first of the month, we've nothing to worry about. I own a mortgage that's due to be paid off then."

"What are you going to do after we've spent that?"

"Oh, the weather'll be too cold for farming and I'll do some serious work at writing. Don't worry about it."

"Who's worrying?" she laughed and kissed me on the cheek. "I knew you were a brainy man the day I heard you tell Lynn how to spell Albuquerque. Imagine, knowing a thing like that!"

We took some of the strain off the family budget by sending Jack back to Washington on a vacation without pay. Thus, we managed to get by until the first of September without running completely out of money. But, instead of a check, I got a note from the real-estate people, quoting some of the small type in our contract which I hadn't read. The sum of it was that I shouldn't expect payment of the note for another sixty days. They said they hoped this wouldn't inconvenience me.

"Oh, well," I said to Connie. "Things could be worse. We've still got about one hundred dollars' worth of food in the house."

So, in order to avoid parting with a dime that we didn't have to spend, we resolved that we wouldn't eat anything that we didn't capture, raise or defrost ourselves. The assortment of food which came with the freezer was quite heady. Our menu featured steaks, chicken, veal cutlets, lamb chops and such fish and crabs as we took out of the river. Our garden vegetables were supplemented by such out-of-season items as asparagas, broccoli and peas. For desserts, we had strawberries, peaches, rhubarb and frozen pies.

"Such hardship as this," I said at the end of our first week on our restricted diet, "I could stand more often."

But after three weeks of the same wonderful food, day after day, the novelty began to wear off. Even Lynn, the least complaining child in the family, finally got fed up.

"Steak again!" she protested when Connie served dinner one night.

"Mommy, why can't we ever have hamboogers?" Claire demanded.

"We can't afford hamburger," Larry said derisively. "Just steak and lamb chops."

About half way down toward the bottom of the freezer, I thought I saw a ray of hope. I had a note from my best friend, whom I had not seen for many months, saying that he was going to be in Washington and would like to visit us.

"He's been making a lot of dough since the war," I told Connie. "Maybe I can float a small loan."

When he arrived, looking as prosperous as a Washington five-per-center, we rolled out the red carpet. For dinner, Connie served turkey steaks, potato puffs and cauliflower, with peach shortcake for dessert. I kicked the children under the table to keep their complaints down and after dinner, my friend observed:

"Boy, you're eating high on the hog. You must be doing all right."

After this, of course, I couldn't put the touch on him.

But when my ever-loving brother-in-law came to spend a week end with us, I refused to keep up any pretense. I sat down before dinner and told him about our financial woes, pulling all the stops. He was properly sympathetic until dinner was served. We were having crab imperial, broccoli with hollandaise sauce, french-fried potatoes and strawberry meringue. Every morsel of it was either out of the freezer or our own hen house.

"Heh, heh," he said. "I should be so broke as this."

"But this stuff is all we ever get to eat," I wailed. "It's the same darn thing all the time. Steak, chicken, chicken, steak, and for variety we can have crabs or lamb chops. Why," I added, rapping my knuckles on the table to drive home the point, "do you realize that this is the third time this week we've had strawberries?"

"Stop it," said the brother-in-law. "You're breaking my heart."

One morning a few days later, I got up on the wrong side of bed and my eye fell on an item in one of our country papers concerning a local political campaign. A well-known radio commentator, who had recently built an expensive home in our county, was conducting a campaign on behalf of one of the candidates. I detested the views expressed by both the commentator and his candidate and, somehow that morning, I felt it necessary to let this be known.

So I wrote a short, barbed letter to the editors of the two county papers, paying my respects to the radio commentator. After mailing the letter, I felt much better. A few days later, the letter appeared in the two little papers and I suddenly found myself a political figure of some proportions in the county.

It was a few days later that the editor of one of the papers, whom I had never met before, arrived at my house looking grim. He said that the radio commentator was incensed by my letter and that he was filing a one hundred thousand dollar libel suit against both papers and me.

After the editor left, I rolled on the floor and roared with laughter.

"My financial standing has improved suddenly," I informed Connie. "There's a man who wants to sue me for one hundred thousand dollars."

"Just mail him those shoes you're wearing," she suggested, nodding toward the pair of ripped, battered work shoes I had on.

"But where would I get fifteen cents for postage?" I demanded.

For a few days this development added a little spice to our quick-frozen diet. Then I received a letter from a firm of attorneys who represented the radio commentator. They informed me that they were giving me a chance to make a settlement of the matter out of court. At this point, I began to get mad all over again. A friend of mine who is a lawyer looked the letter-to-the-editor over and assured me that it was not libelous.

"That's good," I said. "I might have a little trouble laying my hands on one hundred thousand dollars cash right now. In fact, I doubt if I could even spare ten dollars as a retainer for a lawyer."

So I addressed myself to the problem of replying to the letter from the radio man's lawyers. I composed what must be one of the shortest business letters on record:

"Dear Sirs:

Are you kidding?

Sincerely . . ."

I guess they must have been, because I never heard anything more from them.

This little *contretemps* kept our family morale at such a high point that we were able to eat our way down to the bottom of the freezer. The check from the mortgage arrived—and just in time. By then we were so sick of eating frozen food that we couldn't even stand the sight of ice in our water.

The children joined us in a dance of joy around the check.

"All right, all right," I yelled above the clamor. "Mommy's going to the store to buy something for dinner. What'll we have?"

"Hot dogs," one of the girls shouted and the rest took up the chant.

"An' chawklit puddin'," Janie yelled.

"An' tater chips," Claire demanded.

"Baked beans," cried Lynn.

"I thought you didn't like baked beans?" I asked her.

"That was before we got the freezer," she replied.

That night, we sat down to the kind of dinner which would have made a normal family protest that mother shouldn't stay so late at the bridge club. But our faces were beaming as we splashed mustard on our hot dogs and sloshed catsup over the baked beans.

"Now, we're really living," I cried. "Tomorrow we can have hamburgers!"

Chapter 10

*I*N our county, people marry young and soon have large families. But even so, we Toombs were something of a phenomenon.

The first time we visited Leonardtown, the county seat, with the entire family in tow, we brought the creaking wheels of business there to a complete standstill. Connie, I suppose, was chiefly responsible for this. She was thirty years old when we married and a tiny girl with delicate features who didn't look her age. I let her out of the car on the day of our first visit to the town and watched as she swept down the main street, with the children trotting behind.

There was Larry, a little taller than she, walking beside her with his long strides, gesturing wildly and trying to talk her into buying something. Lynn, her long blonde hair streaming out behind, was doing her best to keep up. Cynthia was clinging to Lynn's sash. Behind them came the little girls, their short legs going like pistons and their elbows digging into each other's ribs as they contested for the right to walk on the sidewalk's center crack.

As they passed a store, two or three heads would suddenly

pop out to stare. It was like watching birds pop out of a row of cuckoo clocks. It was impossible for Connie to get any business done until she had satisfied the curiosity of every clerk in town. No one was quite willing to accept the evidence of their eyes that she was the mother of this big family. When she would explain that some were her stepchildren, no one seemed to be able to guess which—although everyone tried.

As time went by, Connie began to get a kick out of the fact that no one would believe that she could possibly be the mother of any except the little girls. But one day, waiting in front of a store for the children to assemble, she fell into conversation with a talkative woman who said that she was the mother of a large family. Connie mentioned that there were five children in our family, but hadn't gotten around to explaining the details, when Larry and Lynn—the oldest and largest of my children—appeared.

"Are these your youngest?" the lady asked.

It was weeks before Connie recovered from this blow.

Finally it became such a nuisance to explain to everyone we met whose children were whose that we generally skipped this question, unless pressed. If a shoe salesman or a soda jerk would comment on how young we were to have so many big children, we simply let it go at that. Of course, we did get some odd looks when it came out that Janie was only six months older than Claire.

Once, we took the big girls to a dental clinic in Washington to see whether their teeth could be straightened. By going to the clinic, we were able to get an examination by an eminent specialist, who would have been otherwise unavailable to us. I made the appointment under my own name, on behalf of Lynn and Cynthia.

There were a few students in the office as Connie and I led our girls in. Cynthia had been reduced to a white fright by the very idea of going to the dentist, so Lynn had promised to go first and show her it wouldn't hurt.

The dentist looked at Lynn's mouth, then beckoned to Connie and looked in her mouth. He had just started to explain to the students how Lynn had inherited her tooth structure from Connie when my bride stopped him. She explained that Lynn was her stepdaughter. So the dentist passed on to Cynthia and then he beckoned me over. I stood there with a mouthful of instruments while he demonstrated conclusively to the students that Cynthia had inherited her teeth from me.

"Who am I to argue with science?" I remarked, as we left. "After such convincing proof that she had inherited her teeth from me, who would believe that I didn't meet her mother until she was six years old?"

"Is that why you never say anything to people when they tell you how much Claire looks like you?" Connie asked.

"A lot of these problems could have been avoided," I laughed, "if we'd married and then had some children, like other people."

Family character develops gradually in homes where people have children one at a time, over a period of years. Both Connie's family and mine each had its own character. When we brought the two together, it was as if a pair of comets had collided, staggered dizzily for an instant and then set off, melted into one, on a new and slightly erratic course.

The blended character of our new family would certainly have been described by a disinterested observer as zany. It was like the sound of oriental music to the ears of a westerner. You knew that it meant something to the audience, but you couldn't quite understand it yourself. I would become aware of this sometimes when we had a visitor.

One night, my father arrived and walked into the living room without our hearing him. I looked up to see him standing in the door way, staring at the family with amazement. I had to look around the room for a moment to understand why.

The radio was going at full blast. Claire was standing in the center of the room with a hymn book, singing as loudly as she could. I had been over in the corner typing a manuscript. Janie was rough-housing with Tonker. Cynthia was walking around the room on her hands. Tenderhearted Lynn was trying to feed bread crumbs to a turtle she had brought in out of the rain. Larry was operating a set of puppets in a rehearsal for a show he was going to put on for the girls. And Connie was curled up in the easy chair, reading a murder mystery and oblivious to it all.

Dad just stood there, shaking his head slowly.

"Hey," I yelled above the tumult, "why don't you kids find something to read?"

"My gosh," replied Cynthia, "it's so noisy around here, I can't find any place to read in peace."

"An' I can't read, even if I've got peace," Janie explained.

Just to add a little spice to the normal confusion, the little girls were always changing their identities. Thus, I might ask Claire to pass something at the table. There would be no response. I would repeat the request.

"Daddy," she would say gravely, "don't you know I'm not Claire?"

"Who are you?" I would ask.

"I'm Virginia, from Heaven."

99

For the next couple of days, she refused to answer us unless we called her Virginia, from Heaven. Then, suddenly, she would become Mrs. Riley from Leonardtown and Janie would be her daughter, Helen. The next day, Janie would be Mrs. Riley and Claire would be the daughter. They would get very angry if we didn't remember their proper identities on any given day.

But I really didn't find out how much confusion these kids could create until I took them to the movies one day. As I recall, the picture was called *The Pink Elephant* or something of the sort.

The opening shot showed a miner driving a small burro along a trail.

"Is that the pink el'phant?" Claire asked.

"No, dear."

"How did the el'fund get pink, Daddy?" Janie demanded.

"Oh, that's just an expression."

"What's a 'spression?" Claire demanded.

"The pink elephant," I replied.

"But you said that wasn't a pink el'phant," Claire protested.

"It's not," I moaned. "It's a small donkey."

"Claire, don't you even know what an expression is?" Cynthia demanded scornfully.

"Sure," Claire replied. "It's a small donkey."

I felt it necessary to straighten the child out on the difference between pink elephants, expressions and small donkeys. By the time I had finished, Claire was paying no attention to me and I had lost track of the movie.

Janie seemed to be having trouble keeping up with the story, also, because she asked:

"What did that lady say?"

"Which lady?" I demanded, in view of the fact that four women were talking at the same time on the screen.

"The one that looks a little like a turkle."

"She said: 'This is my destiny.'"

"What does desny mean, Daddy?" Claire demanded.

By this time, there was a thunderstorm sweeping across the screen and I had a certain amount of trouble explaining over the thunder exactly what destiny means. The movie was getting too exciting for Janie and she hid her face and called on me to tell her what was happening. Cynthia was worried about the way things were going to come out and she peppered me with questions about whether the hero would get there in time to foil the villain, whether the heroine would remember to get off the train at the right station and who would marry whom in the end. But all Janie wanted to know was how soon the cartoon would begin.

Naturally, I did not see much of the movie, but as I left the theater I had a noble feeling that at least the children had understood the picture. But this feeling was quickly dissipated.

"Why did that lady hit that man with that thing?" Claire asked as soon as we were in the car, headed home.

"What lady?" I asked. "What man? What thing?"

"The lady in the movie, Daddy," she explained.

"Oh," I replied, as if I understood, "that was no lady. She hit the man with a mefooble because of the snark in the routine. Understand?"

"I guess so," she said.

"Did you like the picture?" I asked her.

"I didn't at first, 'cept now you 'splained it, I like it fine," she told me.

When we got home to dinner that night, I found that there was no table cloth. Instead, our places had been set on some brightly colored pieces of cloth, which looked oddly familiar to me.

"Some new kind of doilies?" I asked Connie. "They're cute."

"They're dish towels," Connie explained. "Couldn't find a clean table cloth."

I looked at Lynn and Cynthia.

"Didn't I see you girls drying dishes with a clean table cloth last night?"

They nodded cheerfully.

"We couldn't find any clean dish towels," they said.

I know I should have let things alone right there. But I am the kind of guy who will always give a plug hat a kick on April first, no matter how many times I stub my toe. So I looked at Connie sternly and said:

"Last night, you didn't have dish towels, so the girls dried the dishes with a clean table cloth. Tonight, you don't have a clean table cloth so we are eating off dish towels. My question is: where did you get the dish towels today that you didn't have last night?"

"I bought them in Leonardtown," Connie said. "They're cheaper than another table cloth."

"But what happened to those blue doilies we had around here?"

"The girls are using them for wash cloths," Connie said patiently, as if she were explaining something to a backward child.

I had observed that when anything got lost in the house, no one would try to find it. They would just look around until they found something that they could use instead. I was now in the
102

mood to get at the bottom of this and I would no doubt have asked some fool question about what had happened to the wash cloths. But I happened to glance at the knife which had been set beside the pot roast I was about to carve.

"Hey," I said. "This is the bread knife. Where's the carving knife?"

"I was trying to chop some frozen meat with it today and it broke," Connie explained.

"But why don't you use the meat saw on that stuff?"

"Larry was using the meat saw to build a bird house."

"Oh," I said.

"I'm sorry about the carving knife," she said. "It was the only knife we had that was sharp enough to cut linoleum."

Under this system, everything became interchangeable. Connie would use my screw driver to get the top off jelly jars, because the girls were using the can opener to tighten screws on their doll carriages. I would see her using adhesive tape to seal up packages and when I cut my finger, the bandage would be put on with scotch tape. She used up all my dental floss sewing buckles on the girls' shoes. When I came groping out of the bathroom one night, yelling for the face towel that wasn't on the rack, Cynthia handed me a pillow slip with which to wipe the soap out of my eyes.

"Where's the towel?" I growled.

"It happens that the towel is being used for a pillow slip on my doll's bed," she said.

Everyone seemed to be happy with this arrangement except me. I decided I was just going to have to live with it, so I began to fall into the spirit of the thing. I began to use Connie's kitchen utensils for the goats and chickens, made a leash for

Tonker out of the girls' favorite jump rope and kidnaped the scrub bucket to wash the car.

I figured that I was giving as good as I was getting under this arrangement. But one rainy morning, when I was about to set out with Connie on a shopping trip to Leonardtown, I discovered that I was licked. The girls, it appeared, had used my raincoat to build a tepee outdoors and it had been torn beyond further use. This meant I couldn't make the trip that day. It was a disappointment, because I had just decided that the only way to stop inflation in America was to put Connie on a weekly budget. This was the first week, and I wanted to go along to make sure she didn't squander the bologna money on anchovies.

So, after delivering myself of a heart-felt lecture about what was going to happen around the house if people didn't quit using one thing for something else, I sent Connie and the girls off. I gave them strict orders that I was to get a new raincoat out of the household budget that week.

My bride returned some hours later, loaded with bundles and looking as if she had settled the whole problem. As she unwrapped the packages, I discovered that she had bought me a lot of equipment for the farm.

"You take these things right down to the barn for the goats and chickens," she said firmly. "And bring back all my stainless steel pots and pans and the rest of the stuff you took out of the house."

"Where's my raincoat?" I demanded suspiciously. "I can't go out in this . . ."

"After I bought all this junk for you, I didn't have money enough for your raincoat," she said.

"But it's pouring rain," I protested. "What'll I wear down to the barn?"

She looked at me thoughtfully for a moment. I could almost hear the wheels turning over in her head and I knew that my hour of utter defeat was at hand.

"I tell you," she said brightly. "Just take down the shower curtain and wrap up in it. It'll keep you dry."

Chapter 11

T H E R E are some people in this world who cannot be happy without music. Others find life empty without antiques or whipped cream or movie magazines. Connie could manage to get along in the absence of any or all of these things. But she couldn't live without pets.

She is a tender, warm person, who considers herself a sister to all living things. Before we were married, she told me:

"I think you should know that I'll never turn a hungry animal away from our place."

I thought that was wonderful—even though I did not completely share her unbounded enthusiasm for animals.

"We'll have plenty of room," I assured her. "For once in your life, you can have all the pets you want."

The children, of course, were also animal lovers and it seemed to me that joint ownership of pets would help bind the families together and keep everyone happy. It was in this dedicated fashion that our family began to establish one of the most extensive animal collections in private hands since the days of Noah.

My own family had gotten off on the wrong foot in the animal department when we acquired the Beagle hound, Tonker. He was a pretty little dog with an impressive pedigree. Generations of careful breeding had produced in him the ultimate in canine stupidity and contrariness. If Tonker had been the first dog in the world, there would have been no others. I had tried to train him, but in the end he had broken my spirit.

He would neither come when called, nor stay behind when commanded. Every time I concluded that I had finally housebroken him, I was disillusioned. In addition, he was a thief. He cruised around the neighborhood, swiping meat from the stores and the homes of our neighbors with the craft and finesse of a carnival pickpocket. All of this, of course, I was called to pay for. I suspected that some people bought horsemeat, left their doors open for Tonker and then billed me for a leg of lamb. At any rate, I hardly had enough money left to buy meat for my own family.

But Tonker was Larry's dog and that was that.

Connie brought the Emperor Jones into our life. He grew up to be a magnificently malevolent-looking tom cat who would have absolutely nothing to do with anyone but Connie. Jones was a sybaritic, fastidious gentleman who viewed the world with faint disdain. It was beneath his dignity to chase mice, for instance.

"The mice are getting pretty bad," Connie observed one morning as she threw out two loaves of bread and a box of pancake flour.

I had a quaint notion that animals ought to do a little something for their keep and I nodded at Jones and said:

"Too bad we don't have a cat around here."

"Jones is much too royal to chase mice," Connie explained.

The day before Hallowe'en, Connie and the girls went out to look around the countryside for a pumpkin. They were snickering happily when they arrived home and I discovered they had acquired a new cat. It was a young, yellow tom.

"We couldn't find a pumpkin anywhere," Connie said, "and the girls were terribly disappointed. So I got the kitten to make them feel better."

"His name is Pumpkin," Lynn explained, sensing some non sequitur in Connie's remark.

Although Jones kept reminding the new cat that he was a mere peasant, they got along pretty well. But still the mice abounded.

"I guess we'll have to get a female cat," Connie said thoughtfully one day. "They're much better mousers."

I smiled weakly at this news, but she assured me that it was a good idea.

"Jones needs a wife," she said. "He's too royal to go out looking for one."

So we acquired Rita Hayworth, so named because she was going to marry royalty. Rita was good at digging up moles and snaring birds, but as far as I could determine she never laid a glove on our mice.

Finally, I went to the store and bought some mouse traps and it was shortly after this that all of the cats got interested in rodents. You can guess who had to get out of bed in the morning and feed the mice which had been caught overnight in the traps to a pack of yowling cats.

At last, Rita showed signs of being with young. Connie and the girls were wild with joy. Claire kept putting her ear to Rita's stomach.

"Tryin' to hear if the kittens are meowin' yet," she explained.

Connie was especially happy because she thought Jones was about to become a father. I wasn't so sure of this. It seemed to me that he had been off, incognito, doing some royal chasing at the proper time. And I remembered seeing a tired old tramp cat from across the creek sharing Rita's saucer of milk about then.

During the early part of Rita's pregnancy, she suffered from morning nausea. Connie finally persuaded her to go into the bathroom when she felt a dizzy spell coming on. She would meow loudly and whoever was nearest would rush and hold her head.

At last, Rita produced kittens. There were only two of them and the resemblance to Jones was superficial. Connie was quite disappointed, but Rita was ecstatically happy. She took motherhood seriously and, in an effort to provide the sort of balanced diet she felt the kittens needed, she began to drag all kinds of fish life into the house for her young. We would get up every morning to find fish heads, eels and soft crabs scattered around the house.

About a week after Rita's pair had been born, I happened to visit the nursery she had established in my closet and discovered that there had been an increase in her family. There were three jet black kittens that looked exactly like Jones. Connie didn't seem to think that it was unusual, but I got so excited that I reported it to the county papers. Then it was she told me. Rita had not, as I supposed, given birth to separate litters of kittens a week apart. The second litter was something Connie had found floating in a cigar box in the creek.

"That explains where Jones was while Rita was on her honeymoon," I said.

"Rita's happy, anyway," Connie said, nodding toward the mother cat who was trying to haul a fish bigger than herself up from the beach.

In a world where justice is anything more than an abstract concept, Tonker would be the only canine calamity which would befall one family. But worse was yet to come.

The girls had been packing lunches and going down the road to picnic. I was fixing a lunch for them one day when Lynn said:

"Don't forget the extra sandwiches for the dog."

"Sandwiches for a dog?" I demanded.

"Yeah. There's a poor starving dog down the road where we have our lunch. We take him sandwiches."

I had a little talk with Connie.

"Look, Cookie, I know we are pledged to do our utmost for the animal kingdom. But is it necessary to put up a lunch every day for a stray dog?"

"We can't let him starve," she said stoutly.

"It's hard enough remembering how the kids like their sandwiches, but here you've rung in a stranger on me. Tell me, does this dog like mustard on his ham sandwiches?"

"Maybe I should bring him home and feed him," she said.

"Well, it would save on transportation," I said. "But better yet, why don't you take him to someone else's home?"

"I'll bring him here until I can find a home for him," she said promptly.

Dad was around when the dog arrived. The animal was indeed in pitiful condition, but he was a pointer and obviously a well-bred dog. Dad's eyes lit up when he saw him.

"Don't give that dog away," he said with enthusiasm. "He's a good dog. I'd like to have him myself."

"It's a deal," I said. "You can take him back to town with you Monday."

"Oh, he wouldn't be happy in the city," Dad said. "Dogs like that need a lot of space. You keep him for me until I can hunt him and see if he's worth having."

Here was the clumsiest, hungriest dog I had ever seen. He knocked over everything and could be taught nothing. It was impossible to give him enough food and he joined Tonker in meat thievery. Obviously he had led a hard life for he cringed if you so much as looked at him. The girls were delighted with him and Dad, after mulling the matter over, decided to name him Jim, after a pointer he had once owned.

One day, Dad found Jim on the front porch, frozen in a perfect point.

"Look at him," he cried excitedly. "There must be some quail in the yard."

"He's just pointing at a fly," Lynn giggled. "He does it all the time."

Dad refused to accept this statement and took Jim around the yard to see if he could locate the quail. It wasn't long before the pointer came tearing out of the bushes, his tail between his legs. He had found some birds all right—but not quail. He was being chased back to the house by an angry mother mocking bird, who kept swooping down at his head like a dive bomber.

"I don't think that dog of *yours* will ever be much of a hunter," Dad said in disgust.

The girls were so enamored of the dog that they wouldn't let

Connie even try to find a new home for him. So I tried to get used to stumbling over him.

"The more I see of dogs," I told Connie sadly, "the better I like people."

While Connie was content to adopt the more commonly accepted pets, Lynn was a specialist in the less well-known types. She would drag in one-legged hop toads, baby robins with fractured wings, snails that looked unhappy and minnows which had been stranded by a low tide. One day, I collared a couple of turtles in the act of raiding my strawberry bed. I seized them roughly and was about to deport them, when Lynn interceded.

"Could I have them for pets?" she asked.

"If you'll keep them out of the strawberry bed," I conceded.

A few days later, I saw Lynn out in the strawberry bed, picking some of the larger berries.

"What are you up to?" I asked.

"Picking strawberries," she said, "to feed to my turtles."

Larry had a weakness for roosters. He owned one big fellow, named Rocky, who liked to eat people, my flavor. Every time I went into the chicken yard, Rocky would puncture me in two or three places. Later, Larry got a bantam cock, named Brewster the Rooster. The two roosters engaged in noisy crowing contests. Rocky would always find himself in good voice about midnight, while Brewster would cut loose at dawn. Between the two of them, they left few hours of the night when a man could sleep.

All her life Cynthia had longed for a rabbit. Now that she had a new Daddy who seemed to be willing to provide refuge for anything that could fly, crawl or hop, she brought up the subject timidly. She seemed to be quite surprised and com-

112

pletely overjoyed when I consented readily. She got a pair of rabbits which she named Hopalong Cassidy and Drag Along.

"If what I hear about rabbits is true," I said at dinner one night, "we'll be having plenty of fried rabbit before long."

Everyone began to choke on their food and shoot me horrified looks.

"You wouldn't eat one of my baby rabbits, would you?" Cynthia demanded.

All of the girls joined in the chorus of protest.

"In about a year you'll be begging me to eat some of them, you'll have so many," I predicted smugly.

But, as time went by, Hopalong and Drag Along showed no signs of producing any small, frying-type rabbits. Cynthia's maternal instincts were demanding that her rabbits produce a litter of young and she worried and fretted about their infertility. One day, a visitor who raised rabbits was on the place and I put the problem to him.

"I am probably the only man you have ever met," I said, "or maybe ever will meet who owns a pair of rabbits and can't get any little rabbits."

He looked the rabbits over carefully, shook his head and said:

"No wonder. They're both males. With rabbits, it's hard to tell."

I considered my own approach to animals to be more practical. If I couldn't eat them or something they produced, I wasn't interested. So it was that I first added more chickens to our collection. The baby chicks arrived during an unseasonable cold spell and, to protect them, I moved the brooder into the house. Everyone protested that the chicks were too noisy to keep in a bedroom, so we settled them in the living room for a few days.

Following the precepts set forth in my book on homesteading, I invested in a few turkeys which, at the moment they stepped out of their shells, cost eighty-five cents each. Again chill winds forced me to set up the brooder in the living room and it was possible to carry on a conversation only if you could chirp louder than a turkey.

One of the birds didn't get along with his cellmates and, in the course of a Saturday night brawl, had his right eye closed permanently. Being a practical man, I was ready to write him off and wring his neck. But the children insisted that he must be saved. Lynn established a turkey hospital in the living room and appointed me as orderly for the patient. I had to feed him, clean up after him and put drops in his eyes. We named this freak One Eye Connelly.

Connelly lived on top of the phonograph in a card-board box and spent all his waking hours—about twenty-three per day—tapping steadily on the side of the box, like a Western Union operator gone berserk. Lynn decided that Connelly would be happier if we cut a window in the box so he could look out at the big, wide, wonderful world.

Long after the rest of the turkeys had been moved outdoors, One Eye Connelly remained in the living room. Viewed from any angle, he was no beauty. He would pop his head out of the hole from time to time to examine the proceedings with his good eye. Connelly finally served a useful purpose one evening when we had a call from a local character who was somewhat the worse for drink. The man had decided to tell us his life story and was just going around the far turn when Connelly, his neck now as long as that of an ostrich, poked his

114

bald head out of the box, fixed our visitor with a beady, one-eyed stare and gobbled disapprovingly. The man departed forthwith.

The goats, of course, were a part of my effort to own animals, yet be practical. The children looked upon them as pets and Lynn, who often got her tender feelings hurt, would always repair to the barn when she was unhappy and talk her troubles over with the goats. They seemed to be even more understanding than Theodore the Bear.

My homesteading book had told me that goats give milk. That, I finally decided, was merely one of those Great Truths, which we all love so much. It is not a Great Truth that *all* goats give milk. In Phyllis, I had a goat who was not going to give me anything but trouble.

She had her kids one night. It was my first obstetrical case and it was twins, at that. Everything was fine for a couple of days. Phyllis was spouting milk like a fire hydrant and I was happy. But this was as far as she got.

Phyllis began to look sick and stopped giving milk. I summoned the only veterinarian I could find. He confessed that he had never treated a goat before but, since they were like sheep, he prescribed some sheep medicine. This did no good and I loaded her in the car and took her to visit another veterinarian. It was his first goat case, too, and he decided that since she gave milk, he would dose her with cow medicine. He also told me that I would have to give Phyllis a dose twice a day.

I did.

The money that we had been spending at the local store for cows' milk had practically put the storekeeper in the upper-income tax brackets. When Phyllis first started to produce, I

115

thought it prudent to warn him that we would be reducing our order. After all, a cut in our order was bound to have repercussions throughout the Maryland-Virginia milk shed.

It was about a week after Phyllis' event, which by no stretch of the imagination could be called blessed, that I walked into the store.

"Going to have to change the milk order," I told the man.

"Yes?" he said weakly.

"Instead of six quarts a day, you better make it eight. The vet says I'll have to feed the little goats a formula."

So, while Phyllis went dry, I heated cows' milk four times a day and fed it to the young goats. When I wasn't busy feeding them, I was boiling nipples, sterilizing bottles and compounding formula.

It began to occur to me that in this paradise for animals, I was the only one who was contributing very much. The animals had enslaved me, in clear violation of the Thirteenth Amendment. When I wasn't playing nursemaid to the goats, I was hauling feed and water around to the chickens, turkeys and rabbits. The roosters' crowing and One Eye Connelly's drumming kept me awake at night. If I tried to sleep late in the morning, the cats would be howling at my door demanding that I get up and feed them their mice. If I sat down to rest during the day, Tonker or the pointer would start clawing at the door and I would have to get up and let them in.

"As an animal owner," I told Connie, "I'm a flop. These animals own me."

"You don't look very well," she said.

"My stomach's bothering me," I replied.

"Better see a doctor."

It happened that I had to take an insurance examination in

116

town the following week. Connie wanted to go with me and we made arrangements to park the children while we were away. But then we found we had no one to look after the animals. Finally we had to hire Jack to come down from town and sit with the animals.

I talked to the insurance doctor about my stomach trouble.

"It's just your nerves," he said soothingly. "You're worried about something. Look out you don't wind up with ulcers."

"Well, I do have a few worries," I admitted. "All four-legged."

"You live down in the country," he said cheerfully. "Why don't you get yourself a couple of goats? Goats' milk is the best thing in the world for an uneasy stomach."

Chapter 12

*I*N normally established families, the division of duties between mother and father is fairly well defined. But since, before our marriage, Connie and I had both served a double role for our families, the children had forgotten what it was like to have two parents. It took them a little time to adjust to the new family organization.

At first, Lynn and Janie would bring their torn dresses to me for mending and Larry would ask me to cook chop suey or make an apple pie for dinner. Cynthia would take her broken toys to Connie for repair and Claire would run to her mother for protection from an aggressive wasp. Gradually, they got straightened out on which parent was to brush little girls' hair and which was to clear the wash-basin drain when it got clogged.

Being smart children, they soon learned the chinks in our parental armor. If someone wanted something to eat between meals, the request would be put to Connie—for she would let them eat practically anything, any time. If they wanted to undertake some faintly hazardous adventure, they would come to me. I would let them do practically anything, any time. If they were turned down by one of us, they would try the other.

One day, Lynn headed a delegation to ask Connie whether it would be all right to go swimming.

"I think it's too cold, dear," she said.

A few minutes later, Larry came to me and asked:

"Is it all right if I take the girls swimming?"

Not having heard Lynn put the request to Connie, I replied: "Sure, go ahead."

When Connie saw them in the water a few minutes later, she sailed out to call them in. When they informed her that I had told Larry it was all right to go swimming, she called me to account. I had to explain first to her and then to the children.

The next day, Lynn asked Connie if it was warm enough to swim.

"Go ask Daddy," Connie replied.

When Lynn put the request to me, I replied:

"Go ask Mother."

This became such a routine in the household that the children would always ask both of us for permission in cases of dubious undertakings.

"If it's all right with Daddy, is it all right with you if we . . ." the question would be phrased.

"It's all right with Mother, she says, if it's all right with you if we . . ." they would report to me.

As the family began to build up its own code of tabus, the children would ask less and less for permission to do things. Then a new situation developed. Connie would find Larry lying on the living room rug with an open bottle of ink at his elbow, writing a letter of advice to the manager of the Washington Senators baseball team. She would protest, only to be informed that Daddy had told him it was all right. I would scold the little girls for cutting pictures out of a magazine which I had not yet read, only to be informed that Connie had given them the magazine.

"Life sure gets complicated around here," Cynthia grumbled, "with so many parents."

It got complicated for the parents, also. The one thing that the children insisted upon from us was that everything be exactly equal between them. I had to cut a pie with mathematical exactness or I would be accused of favoritism toward the child getting the largest slice. If Connie gave one girl a hug and a kiss at bedtime, she had to be sure not to brush the next child off with a quick kiss or there would be hurt feelings.

At first, we felt as if we were walking a chalk line. But, as time went by, we fell into a more natural relationship. Of course, Connie and I found it easier to identify ourselves with our own children when they had difficulties. Conversely, we could see with some objectivity the mistakes which the other made as a parent. Connie would let me know when I was being too stern and I would tell her when she was being too lenient. We talked these things over in the quiet of our own room and I do not think that the children ever sensed the tremendous effort that we were making to keep things as they wanted them—absolutely equal.

I felt that the children enjoyed the benefit of our effort, however. When my girls needed mothering, they turned to Connie for it. Larry found in her an older sister in whom he could confide secrets that he had never shared with me. Between Connie's children and myself there grew to be a very real, special bond. But there was something in our relationship, it seemed to me, that was missing. I couldn't put my finger on it until one night at dinner when I heard Cynthia ask Connie:

"Mommy, how long is a giraffe's neck?"

"I don't know," said Connie.

I thereupon launched into a learned dissertation on the length of giraffes' necks, having been urged into it by absolutely no one. After dinner, I said to Connie:

"I wonder why your girls don't ask me questions like that? Have you noticed how they always ask you everything?"

"I don't understand what you're driving at," she replied.

"Most kids ask their fathers questions like that. At least, if mine want to know what's the biggest continent they'll ask me. If they want to know whether you put cinnamon in a prune whip, they'll ask you."

"So?"

"That's what I've been missing from your kids. They like me fine. But they don't depend on me for anything. They don't know what I'm here for. I mean, if they asked me tough questions, it would at least show that they knew I had some special purpose around here."

"They'll learn, don't worry," she assured me.

One thing which I felt was perhaps keeping our family divided was the matter of names. Connie, of course, had taken my name, but her girls had not. I felt that this was a little awkward, since it set them apart. I was convinced that Cynthia must have felt this way, also, when I saw her write a return address on a letter she was writing to her grandmother. She put the name "Cynthia Toombs" on the envelope.

Shortly after this I came to a decision. "I'd like to adopt the girls legally and give them my name," I told Connie.

"I'm glad," she said, her eyes puddling up. "I think it will mean a lot to them."

"I don't believe Claire's old enough to worry about it," I explained, "but I'm sure it's important to Cynthia. Our last name has gotten to be something to her like Claire's curly hair —it's something that her big sister Lynn has that she doesn't."

The formalities of the adoption took some time, but there finally came the day when Connie and I went to court and completed the proceedings. I brought home a paper which made me the legal father of two new children—Cynthia and Claire Toombs.

On the way, I did a little shopping for the children and when I got home, I handed out presents to everyone to mark the occasion. Cynthia clasped her package excitedly and then turned to Connie.

"What is it, Mommy?" she asked, as my face fell.

"Why not ask Daddy? He bought it."

"What is it, Daddy?" she asked, looking at the strange lettering on the box.

"It's curly hair for you," I laughed. "A home permanent wave set. You're my real and truly daughter and I'll try to see that you get most everything you want."

Her eyes opened wide behind her glasses and she looked at me as if I had handed her half interest in a toy store.

"Gee, thanks, Daddy," she said, throwing her arms around my neck. "I always thought you'd come in handy some day."

Connie gave her a permanent that evening. Cynthia spent most of her time in front of a mirror for the next couple of days, admiring her wave. But Cynthia's hair being what it was, it began to straighten out before long.

"Mommy can fix it for you again any time," I assured her.

"Oh, maybe I'll let her some time," she said casually.

"Now that she can have curls, she's stopped fretting about

it," I told Connie. "She knows what a permanent wave is for. Hope she'll figure out pretty soon what her father's for."

"She's learning."

"Sure. But I heard her ask *you* at dinner how fast a bird can fly."

A few days after this, I was working in the yard one morning when I heard Claire screaming over on the other side of the house. This was not unusual, but there was a note of fright in her voice. I strolled around to see what had happened. I found Claire clutching Connie's skirts and the two of them were looking with dismay at a young man, who seemed to be talking excitedly.

"What's the trouble?" I asked as I joined them.

"This your kid?" the man demanded unpleasantly.

Claire shot me a baleful look, as if she expected me to disown her on the spot.

"Sure," I replied coldly. "Why?"

Suddenly, Claire let out a bellow.

"He said you'd have to buy a new windershield," she howled. "He said he'd tell on me an' make you pay."

"She thinks she's pretty smart," the man said belligerently.

"Just what the heck is this all about?" I demanded, getting tough myself.

"I had to follow her here," he said defensively. "She wouldn't tell me where she lived."

"I wouldn't get in the car with him," Claire wailed.

"She broke my windshield," the man said.

"Did you, Claire?" I asked.

"No," she sobbed. " 'Cept I was throwin' some little rocks and he droove his car into one of them."

"Show me what's broken," I said curtly.

123

We walked over to the man's ancient jalopy, inspected the dime-sized nick in his windshield and I told him I would pay for new glass. When I had sent him on his way, I walked back to where Claire was standing. Her look indicated that she thought I was going to grab a stick and drive her off the place.

"You better be more careful where you're throwing rocks, young lady," I said, giving her a pat on the back. "This is going to cost Daddy some money."

Suddenly, she relaxed her grip on Connie, looked up at me worshipfully and then took my hand as we walked toward the house.

"I bet you could of beat up that old man," she said. "I bet you could beat up anybody in the whole world, Daddy."

"Well, that's what a daddy's for," I said, hoping that I wasn't committing myself too heavily.

This little uproar was the only one which involved any outside talent. Normally, the children provided all the uproar we could stand. Toward the end of the summer, Connie was beginning to look a little like a combat-fatigue case and when Larry asked us if he could spend a couple of weeks at a summer camp, we agreed with alacrity. Then Lynn and Janie were invited to visit for a few days in Washington with their grandmother. Down to two children now, Connie and I sat back to relax. But we soon made an important discovery. Cynthia and Claire had forgotten how to play together. They stayed under our feet, asking every fifteen minutes how long it would be before the other girls would be back. After two days of this, I called my mother and told her to send Lynn and Janie home. Two bored children, I explained, were making so much noise we were about to go nuts.

It was just a few days before Larry was to come home that our storekeeper drove into our place to deliver a phone message. It was from Larry's camp and I was to call them immediately. I am not a believer in telepathy, but suddenly I knew what had happened. It was just a matter of minutes until I got the call through and confirmed my intuitive fear. Larry was sick and the doctor said he had polio. They would get him to a hospital as fast as possible, they assured me.

Three hours later, I reached the hospital, only to discover that Larry had not yet arrived. The doctor who was to handle the case arrived at the hospital a short time after I did and I began to ply him with anxious questions.

"As I understand it," he said, "the boy has only a slight muscular involvement at present. He has a temperature, his reflexes are slow and he has some pain in his back."

"Does that mean he's going to be all right?" I pleaded.

"No, it doesn't mean anything. He may go along like that for a day, and then get worse. He may go along like that for ten days, and then get worse. Or he may never get any worse. I'm trying to be realistic with you."

While we waited, the doctor told me how pitifully little science has been able to discover about the disease. The only real hope he could offer was statistical. Less than twenty-five per cent of those who get polio suffer crippling aftereffects, he said, and an even smaller percentage are left with any permanent handicap.

Larry arrived at last and the doctor said that he would advise me not to see him, because of the danger of taking the virus home to the other children. A spinal puncture and another examination confirmed the original diagnosis.

125

"We'll just have to wait, maybe ten days before we can be sure," the doctor said. "I'll see him again in the morning and you can talk to me then."

Larry was no worse the next day and I took hope. The following day, he was the same—but the doctor refused to be optimistic. He suggested that I go on home and call him twice a day for progress reports.

"Can't you even tell me that you're sure he's going to live?" I asked.

"The odds are all in his favor," the doctor said grimly.

I found a tense, serious little family when I got back to Dukehart. They all plied me with questions and were relieved when I told them that Larry was not suffering any particular pain. Every morning and every evening, I would steel myself for the trip to the store and the phone call to the doctor. The girls would gather in a silent little circle as I left and would still be standing there when I came back. Always, the news was the same—Larry's condition was the same, but the doctor would not say that the danger was past.

"We're saying our prayers every night for Larry," Cynthia told me as she went off to bed one night.

The ten days dragged by finally and then the doctor assured us that Larry was going to be all right. An orthopedic examination did not show any permanent muscular involvement and I could visit the boy the next day. The girls were wild with joy when I brought the news home and Connie, who had maintained a tense composure throughout the ordeal, broke down at last and cried.

I was a haggard, trembling wreck as I was ushered past the grim iron lungs into the polio ward of the Children's Hospital in Washington the next day. I had neither slept

126

soundly nor eaten well since the day Larry had come into the place. I was searching the ward beds for my afflicted son when I heard a shout:

"Hi, Pop!"

And there, behind a glass partition and waving merrily, was Larry. He looked healthier than I—or anyone I had seen on Dukehart Island. I blinked in disbelief.

"Show your father how you can touch your toes, Larry," the doctor ordered.

Larry reached toward the foot of his bed a couple of times. Then he did a somersault and a few nip-ups and grinned at me broadly. A couple of pretty nurses stood near his bed, giggling at his antics.

"See, I'm all right," he yelled. "You been saving the sports pages for me?"

"*I* should have had polio and *he* should have been home worrying about *me*," I told the doctor as we left.

I raced home that evening and there were smiles on everyone's face at the dinner table.

"Gee, I'm so happy," Cynthia said. "Larry's going to be all right and we'll have the whole family together again."

"We were lucky," I said.

"Mommy," Cynthia said, and suddenly she checked herself and her glance shifted toward me. "Daddy, I mean, what kind of a thing is it that makes you have the 'tile paralsiz?"

"Yeah, Daddy," Claire said, "tell us what does it do? Crawl with legs or fly with wings or what?"

I looked at the two little faces turned toward me. This was a big moment—at last I was in solid. I took a deep breath, because I knew I was going to have a lot of explaining to do—from then on.

Chapter 13

*I*T had been a long, hard struggle, but we finally got the bathtub installed for Connie. To do the plumbing job, Dad had assembled a little bit of pipe, a number of brass bed posts, some rubber hose, bailing wire and a random selection of second-hand plumbing fittings. I recalled that the Wright brothers had fashioned the first airplane out of not much more than this and so I went to work.

There is nothing very complicated about the workings of a bathtub. The water runs in and the water runs out. So, even with the make-shift materials we had on hand, we managed to do the job. I tested it carefully to make sure that here, at last, would be one appurtenance in our house which would have no idiosyncrasy. It was going to be the kind of tub in which any stranger could take a bath without needing ten easy lessons in advance.

When my tests were complete, I notified Connie that the great moment was at hand. Dad, Jack, Larry and I formed an arch with crossed plumber's tools and Connie, a clean towel over her arms, ducked into the bathroom while the children cheered. I waited long enough to hear her splashing about happily in the tub and then busied myself packing up our tools.

It was an unseasonably cold day, with a raw wind from the north, and so I stalled around inside the house for a while. Suddenly, I heard Connie let out a yell.

"Hey, this window won't stay closed," she protested.

"What?" I demanded.

"The window over the bathtub keeps popping open. I'm freezing to death."

When I told Dad about this, he explained to me that it was impossible for such a thing to happen. The window was a new type, which employed springs rather than weights, and was in perfect working order, he assured me. I told Connie that she would either have to submerge or get out of the tub if she wanted to keep warm. When she got out, we went in and found the window open, all right. But when we closed it, it stayed closed. We banged on the walls, ran hot water and even took baths ourselves to complete the test. None of us had any trouble.

The weather was warm for the next week or ten days. Connie spent most of her time in the tub and I heard no further complaints about the self-opening window. But the next time we had a chilly day, the window popped open and left Connie shivering in the arctic blasts. It happened with regularity after that—to no one but Connie. I couldn't solve the mystery. Dad got out his slide rule and tried to work out some coefficient, involving outside temperature, the air pressure of the warm bathroom and the decibel rating of Connie's bathtub soprano. All I know is that after a time, when Connie wanted a bath on a cold day, she would take it in the kitchen sink.

With the bathroom completed, Dad went to work on putting up wallboard and ceilings in the other rooms of the addition. He tacked them in ever so temporarily, of course. As fast as he would get a wall up, Connie would begin to hover near it with a color chart.

"Can I paint this now?" she would ask.

"Oh, heavens no, child," Dad would reply. "I haven't put it up to stay, yet."

But Dad never showed any signs of driving any of the nails all the way in and, as the weeks went by, Connie began to suffer from frustration. Jack finally hit upon the idea of buying her a can of red paint and sending her down to decorate the outside of our barn.

"That'll be right astutable," he assured her. "We built the barn permanent."

This little exercise merely whetted my bride's decorating appetite. One day, she backed Dad into a corner and charmed him into driving a few permanent nails. It was against his better judgment, he said, but he could understand how she was getting tired of living in such a mess.

"I like lots of bright colors," she told him eagerly.

He looked askance at her. His idea of a bright color, it developed, was light cream. Her tastes ran to more exotic ideas, such as salmon pink or emerald green. Dad looked horrified. Finally, Connie asked him what color he would like to have in the room he was to occupy. I'm sure he wanted it mahogany, but he gulped and said bravely:

"Well, if you like bright colors, how about blue?"

"All right," she agreed. "You mix it the color you want, and I'll put it on."

130

Later, she expressed to me her opinion of Dad's choice in colors.

"Blue. Blue. That's all he can think of. I hate blue."

"That's too bad," I said. "I was hoping you'd do our bedroom in blue."

"No more blue rooms," she said firmly.

The girls' room was next, after Connie had painted Dad's blue room. They chose a wall paper that was red, white and blue and Connie put it up like a master craftsman. Then she turned to the problem of painting their furniture to blend with the decor of the room. She rejected red as too garish, white as too ordinary and when I looked in she was painting the furniture blue.

It was some weeks before Connie got around to painting Larry's room. When I walked in to inspect the job, I shook my head and exclaimed:

"I thought you said no more blue rooms."

"This isn't blue," she said indignantly. "It's aqua."

"Can I paint my furniture blue, too?" Larry asked when he saw the room.

"You can paint your furniture *aqua*," she said firmly.

By the time it was possible to paint the living room Connie decided to hire a couple of local workmen to do the job. I was getting a little tired of blue rooms, but she assured me that this was going to be different.

"I think I'll use the rest of that barn-red paint to do the paneling around the bottom and then I'll have to get some color for the top that won't clash with the rug."

"The rug is blue," I protested sullenly.

"It's not. It's dusty aqua."

"If you swept it, it would be blue," I insisted.

"Here's a nice color," she replied, producing a chart. "Sea-foam jade."

"Looks green to me," I said. "But I guess it's all right."

"I think I could add some colors to it," Connie went on thoughtfully, "and get a grayish, blueish, blackish green."

The day the painters were to arrive, I looked at the colors she had mixed up for them. The barn red was red, but the sea-foam jade had taken on a very definite blue look, in my eyes. But I didn't want to start any riots. Connie was the artist and I decided I must be color-blind.

When the painters arrived, she gave them their instructions. The boss painter, to make sure that he understood, repeated them back to her.

"This here paneling is going to be red," he said. "And the top part of the walls and the ceiling you want painted with this here blue."

"It's green," she cried. "It's not blue."

"Yes, ma'am," he said. "It ain't blue."

Finally, Connie got around to our bedroom.

"So there'll be no misunderstanding," I said, "let's paint it white. Put up greenish, pinkish, yellowish wall paper that looks blue to me, but paint the ceiling white."

"But white's such a flat color," she protested.

"But it's the only color I know that can't turn out blue."

She put up the wall paper and, one day when I was in town, she painted the ceiling. Because I got home late, I gave it only a hasty glance and went to bed. But when I awoke the next morning, I lay frozen in bed, staring at the ceiling. I nudged Connie.

"In the daylight," I said slowly. "That white you put on the

132

ceiling has a somewhat familiar look. Sort of a skimmed-milk blue, I'd say."

"I didn't think you'd notice," she said.

"What did you do to the white paint?" I asked grimly.

"Oh, to make it go better with the wall paper I mixed in just a little teeny smidgin of black and green," she said. Then suddenly she sat bolt upright. "Say, it does have a blue tone, doesn't it?"

With the house painted and papered, Connie began to toss out the odds and ends of furniture which, in their quaint way, had been serving us these many years. It was not until she had practically denuded the place that it occurred to me that, as surely as night follows day, some new furniture was going to come into the house now. Sure enough Connie began looking at the furniture ads.

"We can't keep on playing musical chairs forever," I had to admit. "I can never find any place to sit down until someone else gets up."

"Maybe I better bring back that wicker settee you threw on the woodpile," Dad said.

As far as I was concerned, this was the clincher. We bought some new chairs the very next day. But this was only a start and as Connie opened a campaign for new curtains or rugs for the girls' room I would protest that I couldn't afford such things. I had spent enough time at my typewriter to earn eating money—but not re-furnishing money.

"Would it be all right if I bought it with some of my own money?" Connie asked.

Her personal bank account had recently gotten a transfusion as the result of selling the home she owned in a New York suburb. And so, with the small amount of money she had received, she began buying more furniture, recovering more chairs and getting more gadgets for the kitchen.

We were poking through a department store in Washington one day, looking for a lamp shade, when Connie spotted a display of television sets.

Now Connie and I had seen a certain amount of television at the homes of our friends. We had agreed that it was fine— and that it was not for us, just then. I was surprised, therefore, when she suggested suddenly that we look at the television sets in the store.

"Okay," I said. "It doesn't cost anything to look."

"I think we ought to have one," she said. "It would give the children something to do on rainy days."

"Some day, it might be a good idea," I admitted.

A salesman began to show us around, in spite of my protests that we were just looking. Suddenly, Connie pointed to one of the sets and said:

"That's the one I want."

"But honey. We can't afford one now."

"I could pay for it with my own money," she said happily.

"But, even if I let you do that, we ought to shop around. . . . This would be a big step . . . We ought to talk . . ."

I could see that she wasn't listening to a word.

"I like that one," she said.

"Where shall we send it?" the salesman asked, whipping out his order book.

"I think we ought to take it, don't you, dear?" Connie said.

"Wait a minute," I said haughtily. "We're not buying any television set until we've had a chance to talk it over a little."

The salesman put his book away, assumed the nonchalant air of a man who knew there'd be another one along in a

134

minute and I steered Connie toward the door. We hadn't gone far before I was overcome with remorse. After all, it was her own money and if she wanted to burn it in the fireplace, I told myself, it wasn't up to me to stop her. If she wanted a television set, I decided, let her have one. Suddenly, I turned her around and we headed back toward the salesman.

"I'm wrong," I said. "It's your money."

"No," she protested, trying to turn us around again. "You're right. We ought to talk it over, in fairness to you."

"Nope, we're going to buy it."

"No, we'll wait until you make up your mind."

"My mind is made up now."

The salesman didn't seem the least bit surprised to see us back so soon. He wrote up the order and Connie wrote out a check. When we left the store, we had a televison set on the back seat of the car.

"Frankly, the sooner you get rid of this money of yours, the happier I'll be," I told Connie on the way home. "When you're broke, I'll be able to get the family back on a sensible financial basis."

The children went wild when we arrived with the set. The next day, I called a local television man to install an aerial. He put it up, found that we could get only two stations and assured us that if we'd bought the set from him we wouldn't be having this trouble. The aerial cost eighty dollars, but the advice was free.

We explained our difficulty to the store in Washington and they sent a crew of experts down to investigate. When the boss of this crew arrived, he looked at the aerial and asked how much it had cost. After I told him, he gave me a superior smile and said:

135

"We put 'em up like that every day for twenty-eight dollars."

"Well, just see what you can do for us," I said sadly.

His men spent a day working and finally got reception for us on the other channels by installing a second antenna.

"I hate to do this to you," he said, as he wrote out the bill. It was for one hundred and six dollars.

"Oh, well," Connie said as the man left. "It's only money."

"Better still," I replied. "It's only *your* money. And, by the way, how is your personal fortune holding out?"

"It was all right until I got mixed up with this television," she said.

"You know, I've been figuring up what you've spent around here," I said suspiciously, "and I don't see how you had enough left to pay for television."

"Oh, I had just about as much as when I started."

"This," I said, "is something which should be taught in all the colleges. You spend money by the bucket full and still have as much as when you started. How?"

"Well," she said, with the happy air of one who is explaining how she played a tricky bridge hand, "when I'd use my money to buy things for the house, I'd pay myself back with the money you give me to run the house."

"Oh," I replied, since that was about all I could think of to say.

"Well," she sighed, "the money's just about gone, but the place looks a lot different."

I had to admit the truth of this. Our house now looked almost as if *people* might live in it. And, since we had finished work on the addition, it had not been necessary for Connie to sweep up sawdust or scrape dried plaster off the floors every day.

136

"Now that Dad's finished working on the addition," she said happily, "we're really living, aren't we?"

But when I noticed Dad peering around the place curiously that week end, it made me apprehensive.

"You going to stay down here this winter?" he asked.

"I guess so," I said. "I guess we'll have to."

"Then we're going to have to winterize the house," he said.

He spent the rest of the day prowling around under the house and in the attic, tapping walls and measuring windows. The next morning, he was back at it. I was out in the yard before lunch when Connie came rushing up to me.

"Come see what Dad's doing," she babbled and pulled me into the house.

I found him in our bedroom. He had taken down half the ceiling and a couple of sections of wallboard.

"Dad, for Pete's sake, what are you doing?" I demanded, looking at the wreckage of Connie's beautiful paint and paper job.

"We're going to have to insulate this place for winter," he said calmly. "Knew I shouldn't have driven all those nails in."

"And you have to tear out walls to do it?" I moaned.

"Well, some of them," he said.

"You mean we'll have this whole mess to go through again?"

He looked surprised that I should mention it.

"That's better than being cold," he said.

I looked at Connie and she looked at me.

"Oh, well," I said, "it's going to be a long winter. Just think of all the fun you can have painting the house blue again."

Chapter 14

*J*ACK drifted in and out of our life all summer. He would come down with Dad for a week end of work as a carpenter's helper. Sometimes, I would hire him to help me around the farm for the rest of the week and sometimes he would simply stay on as a house guest. Money never seemed important to him. He generally preferred to stay with us at low wages and be happy than to work at a better-paid job in town.

In turn, we were delighted with Jack. I gasped at the prodigious amount of work he could do when he was in the mood and he kept me laughing with his oafish humor. The children loved him because he would drop whatever he was doing in the world of grown ups and descend in a flash to their age level. Connie was fascinated by the glimpses she got of the complicated, sensitive person concealed behind the Simple Simon façade which Jack presented.

During his visits, Jack would invariably get me started on some new farm project out of my book on homesteading. One week, it would be to plant a raspberry bed, while another

138

it would be to plant a pasture for the goats. Or, perhaps, he would look at me blandly and say:

"Ducks are mighty discreetious. Why don't we raise some for us to eat?"

I would take a look at that great big hunk of idle manpower and decide that if he wanted to build a duck pen, I wasn't going to stand in his way. It was always very easy to work while Jack was around to keep me happy. But he would usually go back to town when we were halfway through the current project and leave me to finish alone.

He became like one of the family. From time to time, he would obtain gainful employment in town and we would miss him for a while. He got a job once with a character who traded in farm equipment. Business wasn't very good and Jack was usually paid off in pitchforks or fencing or chicken brooders. He would drag his prize down to our place on week ends and we'd have to figure out what to do with it. We had to build a brooder house so as to have a place for the electric canopy chick brooder he brought once. We had to plant a soybean pasture for turkeys so as to use up the roll of fencing he hauled in another time. One week, he was paid off with fruit trees and we enlarged the orchard.

He finally quit this job, somewhat to my relief. Then he went to work in a soft-drink bottling plant. This work was attractive because he was paid in cash and allowed to consume unlimited quantities of soda pop. At least, he had this privilege at first. But when the company discovered what unlimited quantities he could consume, they began to hedge a little. They only allowed him to drink the flavors that weren't selling very fast.

He appeared one week end and announced that he had quit this job.

"All they'd let me have this week was strawberry," he explained. "It got my allergies all worked up."

Jack's allergies were something of a problem. They went with his moods. When he didn't feel like digging, he would get allergic to dirt and his hands would cause him great pain if he so much as touched the ground. At other times, he would be allergic to milking or to dish water. Then sometimes, goats' hair or dish water would be the only things that would cure the allergy he had acquired to nails or chicken feathers.

But before this week end was over, Connie had discovered that Jack had a more serious problem than his allergy to strawberry soda pop. My bride, by doing nothing more than looking interested, could worm a state secret out of a Russian. Jack finally told her that he had just been involved in an accident while driving his brother's car. So that his brother wouldn't find out—and charge again that Jack was a lousy driver—our boy had put the car in a garage. His problem now was to raise one hundred and fifty dollars to pay the bill and get the car back to his brother on Monday.

"If it hadn't been for that last television aerial, I could lend it to him," Connie said.

"But how would he ever pay it back?"

"I don't know. But it's terribly important to him."

"Maybe he could get it from Dad—advance pay."

"Why don't you hire him with your own money?" she suggested brightly. "Let him work around the farm."

"I thought you didn't approve of spending money on the farm?"

"I don't. But you're doing it anyway. And you might as well help Jack out while you're about it."

It occurred to me that if I had Jack around to do the farm

work, I should be able to step up my literary output and possibly even balance the budget.

I gave Jack a check to cover the garage bill and he agreed to move in and work full time for a couple of months. We would be awakened in the morning by a clattering in the kitchen as Jack searched for a pan in which to milk the goats. This would serve as accompaniment for his early-morning serenade:

"Use Ajax, the foaming cleanser! Wash the dirt right down the drain," he would sing.

The only tunes Jack seemed to know were radio singing commercials. When I asked him why, he told me that most popular songs were about love and he found the subject tiresome.

"Singin' commercials are about all kinds a' things," he said. "Soap and orange juice and cereal. I even know one about a bank. More varietability in 'em."

Jack worked hard during the first couple of weeks of his indenture. We cleared new ground for the garden and built an addition to the barn. In the morning, while he was waiting around for me to finish at the typewriter, Jack would straighten up the house. In the evening, after the chores were done, he would help Connie with the dishes, if his allergy to soapy water wasn't troubling him.

But one morning, I saw him walk past the front porch with a fishing rod and a line. A mouse was dangling from one of the fish hooks.

"Where are you going?" I asked.

"Fishin'," he said.

I shot him a disapproving look.

"Oh, I won't be long," he said.

"What do you expect to catch, with a mouse for bait?"

"Catfish," he said, and walked on.

"Well, let me know when you're ready to go to work," I said sarcastically.

Jack didn't come back to work all morning and, when Connie called "lunch," he was still missing. This was something that had never happened before, so we sent the girls to look for him. They finally found him lying down on a bed in his aunt's house, next door.

"All he did was grunt when we told him lunch was ready," Lynn said.

"My gosh, call a doctor," I replied. "If he's going to miss a meal, he must be a litter case."

"Go ahead and eat," Connie said. "I'll see what's wrong with him."

Fifteen or twenty minutes later, she returned and said:

"He told me he's got a headache and doesn't want to eat. But I can tell he's mad about something."

"Maybe he's mad because there aren't any catfish around these waters," I suggested.

"Did you two have an argument?" Connie asked.

"No, but I got a little sarcastic because he was going fishing during office hours. Did I hurt his feelings?"

"I guess you did. You better go over and make up with him."

But when I went to see Jack, the best I could get out of him was a snort and a guess that he wouldn't be working that afternoon. He not only didn't work, but he failed to appear for dinner. There was so much food left over that Connie decided we could have the same thing for dinner the next day, if Jack stayed mad.

He lived next door for three days. When any of us looked

142

in on him, he would merely turn his face to the wall. Then it got so he would hide when we came to see him. We would find him in a closet, or see him crawl under the house or duck into the bushes. I had to take over his chores, but sometimes I would go to milk the goats and find that he had already done it. Then, I would sleep late the next morning on the theory that he was doing the milking, and he wouldn't show up at the barn.

On the fourth morning of Jack's sulk, we were awakened early by the sound of pots and pans rattling in the kitchen. Then we heard his voice, ringing out loud and clear:

"Oh, brush your teeth with Colgate, Colgate dental cream! For it cleans your breath, while it cleans your teeth."

I groped my way out to the kitchen and found Jack busily mixing up soap and water preparatory to milking.

"What'd you do with me milkin' pail, Doc?" he asked cheerfully.

"So you're back in the world of the living," I observed.

"Sure. Ain't been out of it," he said.

For the rest of the day, he was in high spirits. The only reference he made to his defection came at lunch when he remarked:

"Gotta lotta eatin' to do to make up for what I missed."

So saying, he compounded a sandwich which included cheese, bologna, jelly, peanut butter, mayonnaise, lettuce, pickles and butter.

"Don't you want some catsup on that?" I inquired.

"Sure. And you got any woostersheershire sauce?" he asked happily.

After this, Jack's black moods came more or less regularly. They made farm operations a little uncertain, because I was

143

never sure when he was going to quit for a couple of days. Some days, he would work like a wild man, but other times he would sit around making wisecracks while I did the work. I was never sure whether I was getting too much for my money, or not enough. I began to keep an eye on the calendar and hope that Jack's two months would be over while we were still friends.

For a long time, Connie and I had been working up to buying a new car. I was in the midst of buying a third complete set of parts for Ferdinand the Ford and it was costing me so much in repairs that it was ruining my amateur standing as a consumer. I came by a couple of nice fat checks as a reward for having stayed manfully by my typewriter for several consecutive hours and we decided to blow some of this writing money on a new car.

Connie found a shiny new sedan which the salesman assured her would run even when it was raining—which Ferdinand generally wouldn't. But Jack and I wanted a car that would double as a farm vehicle. I discovered something called a carry-all, which was a sort of station wagon body on a light truck chassis. We were trying to sell this to Connie when a man showed up with a Kaiser Traveler. It was a sedan, but the back seat would fold down so that it could be used as a truck. I saw Connie's eyes light up when she beheld it and I knew that this would be our car.

But she had a birthday coming soon and I figured that by a little sleight of hand I could whip up a surprise for her. So I began to get difficult about the whole thing. I told her that since, for once, this was my money that was being spent, I was going to consider the purchase very carefully. I indicated plainly that we were going to get the light truck. Then I went to the Kaiser agency and told them to deliver the Traveler on her birthday.

Jack was happy when I confided to him that I was buying the Kaiser. But when he found out that it was to be a birthday surprise, his mood changed. Jack just did not like birthdays, nor any holidays, for that matter.

The day before Connie's birthday, he began working himself into a mood. He barely spoke to me and his allergies, he told me, were bothering him something awful. The only thing he felt like doing was to chop down trees. So he went to work on some small trees I wanted removed. When I tried to talk to him, he would merely grunt. Whenever the children went by, he would pitch oyster shells at them. At lunch, he was silent and as he made a sandwich, he merely put sardines, jelly, lettuce and mayonnaise in it—passing up the peanut butter, pickles and honey which he would have included on a normal day.

I wandered down to the spot where he was working after lunch. He was up in a good-sized tree, cutting off the top preparatory to felling it. As I watched him hack away, the top crackled and began to tumble. So did Jack. He landed in a tangle of heavy vines—on his head.

I rushed to his rescue, hoping that he would have nothing worse than a concussion. But before I reached him, he was on his feet, shaking his head hard.

"Hi, ya, Doc," he said, grinning broadly.

"Hurt yourself?" I inquired anxiously.

"Nope, landed on my head."

"That, I could see. Sure you're all right?"

"Sure. That put me back in a good humor," he said, laughing heartily.

I looked at him wonderingly and then gazed up into the tree from which he had fallen.

"Ever do things and then wonder why you shouldn't of done them?" he asked me.

"I guess so," I said, puzzled.

"I was wondering why I stood out on that limb and then chopped the tree out from under me."

"I see what you mean," I admitted.

"Oh, well," he said, picking up his axe. "It put me in a good humor for Connie's birthday."

Early the next day, the new car wheeled into the yard. Connie, expecting to see the truck job, fell on me with kisses. We all piled in to drive down the road and breathe in the wonderful, new-car smell.

"Oh, Daddy," said Janie. "It's beeyoodiful."

"High me up on your lap, Mommy," Claire demanded. "For I can look out the windershield."

"Hey, Pop, when are you going to teach me to drive?" Larry demanded.

That afternoon, Lynn and Cynthia helped me make a birthday cake for Connie. At dinner, we opened her presents and suddenly Cynthia said:

"That car reminds me of a joke."

Everyone looked properly expectant.

"What has wheels and four flies?" she demanded.

We all looked baffled.

"A garbage truck," she replied triumphantly.

"Oh, Cynthia," Lynn protested. "You were supposed to say: 'What has four wheels and flies?'"

"That's what I did say," Cynthia insisted unhappily, "but nobody laughed."

We had to try the new car out the next day, so we headed for town. I pulled into a filling station to get some gasoline and the girls piled out to load up on soda pop. Fifteen minutes later, I heard Claire's voice:

"Mommy, I gotta go to th' bafroom."

I groaned and pulled into the next service station. I bought five gallons of gas, but while I wasn't looking Janie slipped off for another bottle of pop. This meant another stop fifteen minutes later. This time, I ordered gas but they could only get two more gallons in the tank. When the kids ordered me into another service station a few miles up the road, there wasn't room for a drop of oil, gas nor water in the car. There seemed to be only one thing I could buy from the man in return for the use of his facilities, so I bought it—a bottle of soda for everyone.

For weeks before we got the car, Jack and I had been eyeing firewood, sawdust, rocks and assorted bric-a-brac around the countryside. Now that we had something in which we could haul junk, we fell to with a will. Jack brought in yards of gravel for the road and bushels of sawdust for the barn floor. Sometimes, on these journeys, he would load a goat in the back of the car to keep him company.

One day, I sent him off in the car to get the two thousand mile check up from the dealer. It was only a twenty mile trip, but I told him to take his time and make a day of it, if he wanted to do so.

"I guess Jack'll go back to town next week," I told Connie. "I'll miss him—in more ways than one."

"Well, we certainly can't afford to keep him," she said. "You should see the grocery bills I've been paying."

He wasn't home at dinner time but we thought he might

147

have found a movie so we went ahead without him. When we were half way through dinner we heard steps on the porch and Jack entered the house. Behind him came the man who had sold us the car.

"Where you been?" I asked cheerfully. "Have some trouble?"

Jack nodded and the auto dealer just looked uncomfortable.

"Flat tire?" I asked.

Jack answered with a sickly grin. Now I got alarmed.

"Are you hurt, Jack?" Connie asked quickly.

He shook his head negatively.

"Did you have an accident?" I demanded.

He nodded affirmatively.

"Oh, you are hurt," Connie said tenderly.

"Just banged me head," he muttered.

"What about the car?" I asked, growing really anxious.

"It's in pretty bad shape," the dealer said. "In fact, it's just about a total wreck."

"Did you go to the doctor?" Connie demanded of Jack.

"I tell you, I'm not hurt. Just a little bang on the noggin," he insisted, and smiled feebly.

"How much damage to the car?" I asked the dealer.

"Oh, it'll run somewhere around eight hundred or one thousand dollars I'd guess. Your insurance will take care of a good part of it."

"You better lie down, Jack," cooed Connie. "You must feel terrible."

"What about the other car?" I asked.

"There wasn't any other car," Jack said. "I hit a phone pole."

"Isn't your nose cut?" Connie asked.

148

"Just skinted a little," he said. "Now stop fussing over me. Makes me nervous."

"Jack," I said gently. "*I'm* not fussing over you. I'm trying to find out how a cold-sober young man, such as you, could be driving along in broad daylight and run my new automobile into a phone pole."

"I dunno," he said. "I was just driving along when all of a sudden this phone pole just seemed to draw me like a magnet. That's all I know."

And that was all any of us was going to know. For Connie interrupted and said:

"Now don't ask him a lot of questions. He's been through enough, poor kid."

I shook my head slowly.

"Let's have a drink," I suggested.

Connie and I talked it over that night.

"One more week," I said, "and we'd have had our investment in him back."

"Poor kid, he feels terrible."

"I guess I'll just have to let him work this repair bill out, too."

"It'll cost you more than you'll ever get. You can't raise enough around here to pay for him."

"I could put in some money crops. I mean eggs, and chickens and turkeys."

"You better take your loss, before it gets any bigger," she said, reaching for a murder mystery that she had been reading.

"At a time like this, you can read a book?" I asked.

"Oh, I've just got a couple more pages and I'll find out who dunnit," she said.

I lay there in silence for a few minutes, studying the skimmed-milk blue of the ceiling and reflecting on my ill fortune.

Suddenly, Connie let out a yell.

"Hey," she said. "Where's the last page of this book?"

"I don't know," I said. "Where'd you get the book? Sue 'em."

"I borrowed it next door."

"All I can tell you," I said slowly, "is that Jack doesn't approve of murder mysteries. One day, he told me he'd gone through all the mysteries in his aunt's house and torn out the last page."

"I'll kill him," my bride screamed. "Let me at him."

"Now dear," I murmured, putting a restraining hand on her arm, "don't be hard on the boy. He's been through a lot today."

Chapter 15

*D*URING early September, the
weather had been so mild that we had not noticed the approach of autumn. But one morning, we awoke to find a cold
wind blowing from the north and the temperature down. The
wide river seemed suddenly to have taken on a deeper tone
of blue and the wind was kicking up lacy white caps. Out in
the small boat channel, there were dozens of freshly painted
white dory boats at anchor and I knew that the oystering
season had opened that day.

Soon, the weeds in the fields yellowed and dropped their
seed and the wind was heavy with the dry, choking smell of
poplar leaves. The sunsets over the water were so breath-tak-
ingly beautiful that we would sit and watch them, like kids at
a movie. Sometimes at dusk, long wisps of smoke from the
farmers' brush fires would trail across the still, gray waters of
Dukehart Creek. Now, across the creek after supper, I would
see the orange glow of kerosene lamps in our neighbors'
houses, or a shower of sparks out of a chimney as someone
poked the fire.

On chilly nights, we had a wood fire in the fireplace and the children would gather around excitedly to pop corn or to toast marshmallows. To feed the fire, Jack and I would chop driftwood every evening just before supper. Janie was observing this process, in company with a playmate who lived in one of the summer places on the mainland. The visiting child belonged to a family which owned a lumber yard and their fireplace wood was delivered to the house in precisely sawed lengths.

"We got a ol' fashion fireplace," I heard Janie explain to her playmate. "Daddy 'n Jack have to chop th' wood."

One day, Lynn came home and announced breathlessly: "School starts Monday."

This announcement was not enough to put either Connie or me into a panic. We had been stumbling over children all summer long. We now felt that we could get along without them a few hours every day while they were in school. When I had been a boy, autumn had been the melancholy season—for it meant a return to school in the city, with shoes, discipline and boredom. Suddenly, I decided that autumn might not be so melancholy, after all.

With Jack on the premises full time, laboring to repay the money I had spent to repair the new car, we had gone ahead at a good rate in winterizing the house. We had buried the water pipes, installed a floor furnace and plugged up holes in the clapboard. We had even smuggled a couple of carpenters into the place from Monday until Friday of one week to help insulate the ceilings. But Dad discovered this and he got so upset that we had to let them go. Thereupon, he got into the act. The result was that while Connie was shampooing the girls' hair, the water would go off suddenly and we would

152

know that Dad was tinkering with the plumbing. If the electricity was shut off in the middle of an exciting TV program, we'd know that Dad had blown a fuse fixing the wiring.

I did my best to prepare Connie for the school that her daughters were about to enter. My children had already spent some little time in this school, but Connie had only a faint notion of what was coming when we deposited our children there the first day.

Now I am no authority on schools in rural America. But I doubt if facilities anywhere in the country are any more primitive than those my bride found that first day in St. Mary's County, Maryland. If so, they would have to be designed for the specific purpose of making education impossible.

The ancient, drab frame building which housed the school was set back deep in the woods. It had no electric lights and, during the dark days of winter, it was sometimes impossible for the children to read. There was no running water and the well which was supposed to supply the school had almost run dry. A trickle of water came out of a moss-coated pipe and dripped into a turgid pool. Teachers warned the children to bring their own drinking water. The toilets were out of doors —Chick Sale types. Heat was supplied by a couple of pot-bellied stoves, which the teachers looked after themselves.

The only thing that made this creaky antique into a school was the lady who ran it. Miss Louise, a purposeful but tactful lady of middle years, was the principal and one of the two teachers who handled all six grades. During the past twelve years, she had never missed a day of school. Somehow, she gave you the feeling that even if the school had been conducted in a cave, her pupils would have learned *something*.

Stately Lynn, who had once learned to curtsy and say

"Bon Jour" at Madame Somebody's school for young ladies, was the only one of our girls who looked entirely at home as we left them at the backwoods school that first morning. Cynthia, accustomed to the crisp, efficient ways of a suburban New York school, was completely baffled. Claire and Janie, in their first year out of what they called "kidney garden," stared with fascination at the half-dozen quaintly dressed Amish children who attended the school.

But all our girls adjusted quickly. They left the house at 7:45 A. M. to catch the school bus and didn't get home until nearly 5 P. M. Larry was starting junior high school; however he rode the same bus with the girls. The little girls would march off proudly enough in the morning, swinging their lunch boxes and books, but they were dragging by the time they got home in the afternoon.

I had a new duty now in the evenings—helping the girls with their homework. I seemed to be of help to everyone but Cynthia. She was forever getting things so confused, in a logical sort of way, that I would wind up in a heap on the floor. One night, she brought me her arithmetic paper to correct. She had two rows of subtraction problems and I went over them, gravely marking them all correct. Then, I looked at the paper for several minutes, sensing that something was the matter. Suddenly, I discovered that she had done the problems backwards—and I had okayed the whole process—subtracting numbers like 1949 from 1830.

Another night, she called across the living room:

"Daddy, how many bushels in a peck?"

"Let me think," I replied. "Is it two or four, Lynn?"

"How many bushels in a peck, Daddy?" Lynn whooped. "There are four pecks in a *bushel!*"

"From now on," I said, "you help Cynthia with her arithmetic. It's too confusing for me."

Our dinner-table conversation was enriched by the full life the girls were leading in school.

"What did you little girls learn today?" I asked one night.

"I learned to skip on two feet today," Janie said. "It's funner 'an jes one foot."

"I learned something, Daddy," said Cynthia. "How do you divide two oranges equally among three people?"

"Is this arithmetic, or one of your jokes?"

"Sort of both. Do you know the answer how to divide two oranges?"

"I give up."

"Make lemonade," she said.

"Cynthia," Lynn said gently. "The answer wouldn't be orangeade, would it?"

"Oh," said Cynthia, looking in wild alarm. "Well, why is everybody laughing?"

"I ain't laughin'," said Claire.

"You're what?" Connie said, giving her a look of mock horror.

"I ain't nothin'," Claire said. "I said I ain't laughin'."

"You mean I'm *not* laughing. We don't say 'ain't.'"

"Well, the kids at school say 'ain't.'"

This was simply the beginning. For we discovered that whatever knowledge of grammar the children managed to pick up from Miss Louise in class, they quickly rubbed off at recess with their playmates. Our smaller kids came home, chattering in the dialect which is entirely intelligible only to the rivermen and farmers of this section of Maryland.

Lynn made cookies one day and slipped a sample to Cynthia.

"What's inta these here thangs?" Cynthia asked casually.

"Cynthia, what did you say?" Lynn demanded incredulously.

"Thangs—thangs. Are you deaf?"

"Cynthia, what are thangs?" Lynn said slowly.

"That's the southern language," she replied pertly. "Don't you even understand the southern language?"

But grammar was not the only subject in which the girls were getting an education. The little girls, who had never given the matter any attention before, began to talk about love and their fellas.

"I've got three people in love of me now," Claire said at dinner one night. "I'm so werried!"

We could tell, knowing flirtatious Claire, that it was the kind of worry one experiences when faced with making a choice from a tray of assorted French pastry.

"I've got five of 'em in love of me," replied Janie, who was not going to be outdone. Then she gave her hair a casual flip in back and added nonchalantly: "But, I'm not werried. Let 'em love me. I don't care."

Sometimes, if the weather was bad, I would run the girls up to their little school in the morning. When our car pulled into the school yard, all the pupils would gather around excitedly. The Amish children, afraid that they might commit a sin by getting too close to the car, would hang back. The little Amish girls, in their long blue Mother Hubbards, would stare at us from under their droopy sunbonnets. The Amish boys, uniformly clad in dark-gray trousers, blue work shirts and suspenders, would touch their black pork-pie hats in a salute of some sort.

I was curious too about a couple of over-sized boys I saw at the school. The girls told me that they were merely serving out

156

their time until they were old enough, under the State law, to quit school and start farming. One of them was fourteen years old. He was in the fifth grade. In the fourth grade, there was a thirteen-year-old. A substitute teacher came to the school one day to take over for Miss Louise's colleague. She was young and just out of teacher's college. The fourteen-year-old fifth grader looked at her carefully for a time and then he said suddenly:

"Oh, now I remember you. You was goin' to school here when I was in the firs' grade."

I had to tell Connie that, when winter came, there was a delicate problem which would arise. One or two families whose children attended the school just quit taking baths during the cold weather. These children carried lice in their hair.

"Now Lynn, you know which kids they are. I want you to show the other girls so they can stay away from them," I told the family.

"Oh, that wouldn't be very nice," said Connie. "Think how the poor children will feel."

"I'd hate to think how you'll feel the first time one of ours comes home scratching," I growled.

"But it's not the children's fault," she persisted. "I don't think it would be nice if they had to suffer."

"Girls," I said. "Be nice to the children who have lice. Smile at them, talk to them, throw a ball to them. Don't make them feel bad. But for Heaven's sake, don't get too close to them. Is that okay, Mommy?"

"Well . . ." Connie replied dubiously.

A public-health nurse came to the school at intervals, to apply DDT where needed and to conduct other routine physical examinations. She came to give the children eye tests one day. There was one little girl who refused to take the test.

157

"But you might need glasses," the nurse told her.

"Why?" the child demanded.

"To make you see better."

"I reckon I can see aplenty now," the child said, and marched back to her seat.

Connie packed lunches for the children and this was a job which required unusual mental effort. They all had some special prejudice. One wouldn't eat a peanut butter sandwich if it had butter in it, while another would eat peanut butter only if it had jelly on it. Two of the girls liked mayonnaise, and two of them wouldn't eat a sandwich with mayonnaise. Connie was forever passing out the wrong lunch to the right child. Finally, she got so that she would make up a week's supply of sandwiches, put each girl's name on her sandwiches and keep them in the freezer.

Connie tried to make sure that the lunches included something that was good for the girls, such as carrots or fruit or celery. These items were considered a great novelty by some of the other children, whose normal lunch might consist simply of cold biscuits or boiled potato sandwiches. The most amazing lunch was that which the school fat boy brought. His mother sent him off every day with a quart of home-canned peaches and a dollar bill. He stopped at the country store and spent the money on soda crackers, vienna sausage, sardines or whatever struck his fancy. He would also buy half a dozen candy bars, or perhaps a pen knife, which he would present to his girl friend of the day.

Sometimes, after Connie had sent the girls off with a particularly nutritious lunch, she would discover that they were coming home hungry. Then we would learn that they had turned most of their lunch over to some starving dog or cat they had encountered along the way. One day, after Connie had risked my wrath by making sandwiches out of some high-priced cream cheese and olives she had smuggled into the house, she asked the girls how they'd enjoyed the luxury.

"Oh, I traded my sandrich to Cordia," Janie said casually.

"What sort of sandwich did you trade it for?" Connie asked.

"No sandrich. She guv me a biscuit with melty butter and some persimmunds."

"An' I traded with Myrtle," said Claire.

"What did you get?" asked Connie.

"A rabbit sand'itch. Her Daddy went ahuntin'."

"And he killed a poor little rabbit?" Lynn demanded in outraged tones.

"Uh-huh," replied Claire. "It was gooder 'an cream cheese and olives, too."

"Claire, that was mean to eat a poor little rabbit," Cynthia said, chorusing Lynn.

"There ought to be a law against shooting little bunnies," said Lynn, now on the verge of tears.

"When I get married," Cynthia said, pursing her lips and speaking with vehemence, "I'm going to marry a man that doesn't hunt at all. Fact, I'm not even going to let him have a gun in the house. There's going to be strictly no killing at all in my house, unless my husband's a policeman and just kills people."

"Well," Claire chattered. "I'm not goin' to let my husbin do anythin', 'cept what I let him do. Least, if he wants to go far off away an' shoot a rabbit, well I guess 'at's all right. But I won't let him kill any chickens. Least, won't let him chop their heads off out on the front lawn while I'm eatin'."

"I didn't eat my lunch today, Mommy," Lynn said quietly.

"Feeding another dog?" I asked.

"No, I gave it to Joanne."

"Who's Joanne?" Connie asked.

"Probably some child who only gets hay sandwiches," I suggested.

"She doesn't even get that," replied Lynn. "She doesn't have any lunch, usually."

"Yes, she's real poor," said Cynthia. "I feel sorry for her."

"She's too poor to have any lunch?" Connie asked in alarm.

"Sure. The best she ever has is a cold sweet potato. Usually, nothing."

"Oh, I bet I know who that kid is," Larry said. "She's the little skinny one with the runny nose. Her old lady's always drunk."

"Well, I'll put some extra sandwiches in your lunch for her," Connie said.

"And she's not the only one who doesn't get enough to eat at our school," said Cynthia.

"Gee, it's unbelievable, isn't it?" I said.

"I'll pack extra sandwiches for all of you," Connie said. "You can pass them around."

"Now wait a minute, Honey," I said. "You can't feed the whole darn school."

"You don't want me to let those children go hungry, do you?" she demanded.

"No," I said quickly. "Don't get me wrong. I just mean, there ought to be some better way to do it. What happens to all this food the government buys up? Isn't that passed around for school lunches?"

"Sometimes we get a few apples," Lynn said.

"But what about all the potatoes and butter and eggs?" I de-

160

manded. "With children going hungry in this country, what happens to all that stuff?"

"They give it out for school lunches, Pop," said Larry. "I saw that in the paper the other day."

"Well, why don't we get some for our school?" I asked Connie.

"They used to serve lunches at school a couple of years ago," Lynn recalled. "The PTA did it."

"There," I said triumphantly to Connie. "You see, there's a better way to do it. Just go to the next Parent Teachers Meeting and get the lunch program started again."

"Who, me?" she said faintly. "I'm supposed to tell the PTA what to do?"

"There's a meeting next week," said Lynn. "Miss Louise wants you to come."

Connie went to the meeting and before she knew what was happening there was an election of temporary officers and she found herself secretary. Miss Louise admitted gravely that some of the children were getting inadequate lunches and it was agreed that a committee would work out a plan for serving lunches. Since whatever Government surplus food that trickled down to St. Mary's County consisted of dried milk, a few bags of potatoes or an occasional barrel of apples, it was obvious that the PTA would have to raise money to buy most of the food.

The best way to raise the money, it was decided, was to raffle a turkey before Thanksgiving. There arose then the question of who would supply the turkey. I was sitting well back in the room, hoping that no one would notice me. I considered the possibility of volunteering a turkey from the two survivors which remained of my dream of a Thanksgiving dinner. But then I reflected that these birds had cost me so much that they would have been worthy as a prize for the Irish Sweepstakes. A farmer, who had done better than I with his turkeys, offered one as a prize and it was decided that the children would sell the raffle tickets. After a lot of irrelevant discussion, the meeting adjourned.

Our children, armed with raffle books, made life unbearable for everyone in the community. The little girls were particularly formidable as a team of ticket salesmen. They would knock on a neighbor's door and one of them would make a sale. Then the other would look so unhappy because the order wasn't out of her book that the customer would have to buy a double dose.

I steadfastly refused to buy any chances, on the theory that I needed another turkey like a hole in the head. Finally, I broke down and agreed to buy the last ticket out of each book sold, if the girls would guarantee that I wouldn't win.

Shortly before the drawing was to be held, there was another meeting of the PTA. This time, permanent officers were to be elected. Connie had a headache on the night of the meeting and instructed me to attend and withdraw her name from consideration for re-election as secretary. When I came home from the meeting, she asked:

"Did you get me out of the secretary's job?"

I nodded affirmatively.

"Thank heavens," she sighed. "Who was elected president?"

"Me," I said glumly.

When the girls found out that their father was the new president of the PTA, they redoubled their efforts to sell raffle tickets. It became a matter of family pride. The harder they worked, the greater grew their concern for the children who weren't getting enough to eat. One night at dinner, I was trying to explain to them how universal was the problem of hunger and poverty which they saw in the county.

I remembered an article I had just read in a news magazine about a poorly paid barber in New York who was giving most of his time and money to sending packages back to needy people in Italy. I told them the moving story of how much good this simple man had done and how revered he was by the half-starved, paper-clad children he had helped in the old country.

After dinner, Cynthia came to me and handed me two dollars.

"What's this?" I asked in surprise.

"It's the money Lynn and I were saving to buy a mother rabbit," she said. "We want you to send it to that barber man so he can buy food for those Italy children."

My eyes filled up and I drew the two girls close to me. Finally, I looked up at Connie and said:

"You remember the wish I made on the moon that first day down here?"

She nodded.

"I said I wouldn't tell you what it was until we'd been married for a year. But I'll say this—it's coming true."

She smiled and said quietly:

"So is mine."

When the day came that the children were to turn in their raffle books, everyone had sold their quota except Cynthia. She still had fifty cents' worth of chances to sell, and I suggested that she might dispose of them to some of the high-school children on that bus that morning.

"Get Larry to help you," I suggested.

"Okay, Pop," he said gravely. "We'll see what we can do."

As he was leaving that morning, he touched me for some money to buy school writing paper and I handed him a dollar, with instructions to return the change.

When the girls got home that day, they were highly excited.

The raffle money had totaled something over one hundred dollars and apparently the lunch program was now assured.

"The drawing's tomorrow," Lynn said. "Miss Louise said to be sure and be there."

"Okay," I replied. Then I asked Cynthia: "Did you sell the rest of your tickets, dear?"

"Well, uh . . ." she giggled.

"I got rid of 'em for her, Pop," said Larry. "In fact, I bought 'em from her."

"I told you I don't want to win a turkey," I moaned. "I'll give them money, but . . ."

"I didn't buy the tickets for us," he said brightly. "I bought them for Joanne. Her old man wouldn't buy any tickets, so I bought the rest of the book for her. With the change from that dollar of yours."

"Well," I said dubiously.

"I think that was nice of Larry," Lynn said stoutly. "If Joanne should win, she'd get something to eat for once."

Connie and I went to school for the drawing next day. One of the small children stepped up to a huge kettle and drew out one of the raffle slips. Miss Louise took it from the child, glanced at it quickly. Then she looked at me, and for an instant the flicker of a smile played around the edge of her purposeful mouth.

"Joanne is the winner," she said.

She crumpled up the slip and a few minutes later, I saw her drop it in the stove.

The girls went home from school with us that afternoon. When Larry arrived later after his ride on the bus, they burst forth to tell him the good news. He came in the house grinning and clapped me on the back.

"See, Pop, everything worked out all right, didn't it? You're not sore at me now for spending your fifty cents, are you?"

"I never was sore," I said. "It's a good feeling to be generous."

"It sure is," he agreed.

"But," I continued. "You'll really feel swell when it's something of your own that you're giving. Like Lynn and Cynthia did with their two dollars for the barber. So next time you want to be generous, be sure that it's your own money you're handing out. Then you can have that good feeling."

Larry reached in his pocket and pulled out a quarter of his allowance.

"Tell you what, Pop," he said, handing me the money. "I'll give you this and then we can both have that good feeling."

Chapter 16

C ONNIE was a quiet girl, who had the unusual habit of listening to what people said to her.

Because she would listen, and speak back with sincere sympathy, total strangers would suddenly begin blurting out their life stories to her. If she were sitting in the doctor's office, the woman next to her would begin to describe her symptoms. Connie would commiserate and the strange woman would suddenly confide the grisly details of some family scandal. While Connie waited at the store for the mail, some neighbor she barely knew would begin to tell her side of the quarrel she'd had with her husband the night before.

It was a while before Connie began to get really acquainted with some of the more unusual people around our creek. We were passing the home of a neighboring farmer one evening. In a rocking chair on the front porch, we saw a huddled figure, clad in overalls and an old work coat. From under a straw hat, we could see a pipe protruding.

"Good evening, Mr. Bryant," Connie called out.

There was no answer.

"Not very friendly, is he?" she observed a few moments later.

"That was Mrs. Bryant," I explained. "Better known as Miss Annie."

"Oh," Connie replied contritely.

One day, we had a visit from a waterman who lived across the creek. He wanted to work out some sort of agreement with me, to run for a twenty-year period, about trapping muskrats in the marsh behind our house. I talked to him for a long time, but wouldn't be pinned down to an answer.

"Why didn't you let him do whatever it was?" Connie clucked sympathetically, after the man had gone.

"I couldn't see much point in a twenty-year agreement," I said.

"Why not?" she asked wonderingly.

"He's eighty-three years old," I explained.

One afternoon, a sulky-faced young lady, with whom we had a nodding acquaintance, came to call on Connie. After making the usual observations about the weather and the state of everyone's health, Connie settled back to wait for the gusher of confidences which she expected would follow. But the girl said nothing more than "Yes, ma'am," "No'm," and "I reckon so."

Nothing that Connie could say would produce more than a monosyllable or two. Finally, they resigned themselves to an uncomfortable silence, staring at the floor for five or ten minutes at a stretch without uttering a sound. An hour of this left Connie badly shaken and she finally managed to get her visitor started toward the door.

At this point, the girl screwed up her courage and asked if Connie wanted to pay her a small bill we had owed her husband for some work he had done for me.

"I was so relieved to find out what she had on her mind, I nearly got hysterical," Connie told me.

"We don't owe them any money," I observed.

"I know," Connie said. "I remember paying him one day down at the store. But he was about half-tight and he probably forgot to mark it off on the books."

"But Honey," I said.

"If I'd told her that, they would probably have had an awful fight about it," she said.

As Connie's reputation as a Lady Bountiful began to spread, we found ourselves the recipients of a number of odd consignments—animal, mineral or vegetable. As a consequence, we knew we would send five children off to school in the morning—but we had no idea what would come home that afternoon.

Children at school would entrust injured birds or frogs to tenderhearted Lynn, with the assurance that they would find a good home with her mother. Neighbors would thrust stray cats into the arms of the girls for delivery to Connie. When our friends had a baby who needed watching, they would drop it off with us. The children were bringing home a steady procession of over-night guests.

Naturally, even we couldn't keep all the animals that landed on our place. So that part of the children's time which wasn't devoted to collecting strays was given over to finding new homes for them.

Claire and Janie were the champions in the latter field. The little girls would start off with determined looks on their faces. They would beat on every door for miles around until they found a home for whatever surplus kittens, bantam roosters or pet possums we had. The day any storekeeper or farmer needed a new mouser, the little girls heard about it and delivered.

However one day the children's passion for collecting led us into deep waters. This had its inception when the girls came home from school with a note to Connie from Joanne, the pitiful child whose plight had led to the school-lunch program.

The note was written on a piece of school paper in the childish, penciled scrawl of a ten-year-old:

"Dear Mrs. Toombs,

"I wish I could know you because you are so kindly. I have a mean stepmother who beats me and doesn't give us anything to eat. I wish I could live at your house.

Joanne."

For several days after she received the note, I would see Connie gazing off into space from time to time. When I asked the reason, she told me that she was thinking about Joanne.

"I just can't get that note off my mind," she said.

Soon it was her turn to go to school and help serve lunch, so Connie sought out Joanne and had a talk with her. She came home from this interview even more disturbed.

"Isn't there some kind of welfare agency down here to help a girl like that?" she asked me.

"Not really," I said. "Unless you could show that she was being tortured or something awful."

"Well, she did show me a scar on her head where her stepmother had hit her once, and then rubbed kerosene on it. But that was a couple of years ago."

"What is the set-up, anyway?" I asked.

"Oh, it's one of those terrible homes. Tenant farmers and they've both been married before and have Heavens knows how

169

many children running around. The mother gets drunk and then the father beats her and then the mother takes it out by beating his children."

"Yeah, there's a million like them," I said sadly.

Late one Friday afternoon, Cynthia and Janie burst into the house, home from school before the others.

"Joanne's run away from home," Cynthia said, so out of breath she could speak no more.

"Oh, Cynthia," stormed Janie. "You've ruinded everythin'. I was goin' to tell Mommy."

"Okay," Cynthia panted. "You can tell the rest."

"An' she's comin' to live with us," Janie said.

"Take it easy," I said. "Tell us slowly."

When they'd caught their breath, they told us that Joanne had decided that she couldn't stand her home any longer. The girls had suggested that she might as well come and live with us.

"She's comin' down th' road with Claire, now," Janie said. "She got away jes' in the neck of time. Her stepmother was goin' to kill her."

We greeted Joanne casually when she arrived, as if she were simply coming for supper. But after the meal, Connie had a talk with her and discovered that she had, indeed, decided to run away from home and had come to live with us.

"But this is silly," I said. "You can't take in children, the way you do stray animals."

"But we can't make her go home," Connie protested.

"Honey," I said. "This is like kidnaping. There are a lot of rough people down here. There's liable to be trouble about this."

"We can't send her home. She's really afraid they'll kill her."

"There'll be a posse after her by morning."

170

"What can we do?" Connie said piteously. "We can't drive her back to face that. You should hear the kid. She's like a frightened little rabbit. My gosh—what she's been through!"

"Maybe I could tell her people that she's spending the week end here. Then we'd be in the clear and she wouldn't be in trouble when she goes home."

But none of my children knew where Joanne lived. The directions Joanne gave me for reaching her house were so devious that they would have taken me nowhere on dry land. So I decided I would simply have to wait until morning.

I sallied down to the store the following morning, expecting to learn that the sheriff had been around with bloodhounds. But the storekeeper had heard nothing about a missing child. So I went to Miss Louise's home to confer with her on the situation. No one had been to her to ask about Joanne, she said, and until I had come, she did not suspect that the child had not gone home.

"You'd better take her home," Miss Louise declared. "Looks to me as if you've got enough children down there already."

"Well," I said uncertainly. "We don't like to drive her away. Maybe I'll go to see her father, at least, and tell him where she is."

"You'd better be careful," she said. "I understand that's a pretty rough crowd."

Miss Louise told me how to find the child's house. But when I got there, no one was home but the children. I told one of Joanne's sisters where she was and the girl explained that her parents had left before dawn to take some corn to Washington.

"Your father didn't miss Joanne?" I asked.

"He'd a sure missed her if he'd knowed she was gone," the girl explained.

So I told her we would keep Joanne over the week end and send her off to school Monday.

When I got home, I found that Connie had bathed and shampooed the child and dressed her in some clean clothes. She was playing happily with our girls, squealing with joy over each new toy they brought out for her. At lunch and dinner, she put away such quantities of food that even Jack was amazed. She sat by the television set that evening, staring in fascination. Joanne, in our home, seemed to be living in a beautiful dream. And she made it clear that she didn't intend to let it end.

In the dark of the night, Connie and I lay awake talking about her. Connie had taken the child to her heart and had decided that she must stay with us. I tried to convince my tender-hearted bride that such a thing was impossible and to tell her why.

"It's rough," I said, feeling like a Scrooge. "But she's just got to go back home and face it. The best we can hope for is to help her learn to live with her people without suffering too much. And maybe we can help her find a better place some time."

"I just can't send her back," Connie said. "She'll be crushed in that place. If someone would only adopt her."

"Who's going to adopt her down here? Everyone's got all the family they can handle now."

"We're the only friends she's ever had. We can't let her down."

"I know. I know. We'll find some way to help her. But you tell her she's got to go home Monday and sit tight until we can figure something out."

Connie told Joanne this the next day and assured her that she needn't be afraid to go home. We sent her off to school on Monday with our girls and then sat down to find a solution for the problem.

Late in the afternoon, a little before the time when we would

172

normally have expected our children home, a car drove into our yard. Lynn, Cynthia and Janie jumped out, followed by the teacher who assisted Miss Louise.

"I'm afraid that there's been some more trouble about Joanne," the teacher said. "She's run off again."

"She told us she was going to come back here," Cynthia said breathlessly.

"An' Claire's run away with her," Janie added.

Connie and I exchanged looks of alarm and then sat down to listen to the story in detail. Joanne and Claire had disappeared into the woods while waiting for the school bus. This time, a posse was forming to search for them. Since Joanne had told the girls that she was coming back to live with us, the search was being directed along the road toward our house.

Within an hour, Miss Louise arrived with Claire in tow. She had been overtaken, but Joanne had slipped away. Miss Louise said that several parties of men were beating the brush for her and that her father had joined the search.

"Why did you run off?" I asked Claire.

She was wailing and finally sobbed:

"I was goin' to bring Joanne here, for she wouldn't have to go home an' let her stepmother kill her."

Every few minutes, a breathless courier would pull into the yard to bring the latest reports on the child hunt. She was being seen—each time just a little closer to our house—but was moving so cunningly that no one could catch her.

It was nearly dark when a battered old car pulled into the yard and disgorged a red-faced, formidable-looking man.

"Are you Toombs?" he demanded angrily.

"Yes," I said, trying to keep my voice calm.

"Know anythink about this here little girl?"

"Who are you?" I asked, playing dumb.

"I'm her daddy. Where is she?"

"I don't know. She was here for the week end."

"You ain't seen her this evenin'?" he demanded, glowering at me.

"Nope. We told her to go on back home and stay with you."

Suddenly, his belligerency departed. When Connie joined the group, he took off his hat and spoke gently to her. Within a few minutes, he was pouring out the miserable story of his life to her and sparing no details. After listening to fifteen minutes of it, I was feeling as sorry for him as I did for his daughter.

His tale was interrupted by the arrival of a messenger who reported that Joanne was surrounded in a patch of woods just a few hundred yards from our island, but that she wouldn't come out.

"Poor kid, she's like a hunted animal," Connie said.

"I don't know why she carries on like this," the father whined. "I never beat her in my life, onless she needed a switchin' like any chile."

Connie and the girls walked up the road, calling "Joanne" but they couldn't get her to show herself. Finally, the school bus driver found her lying under some vines in a ditch and dragged her out.

"Gimminy," he muttered to me as he turned the child over to her father, "I didn't know whether to hold on to her or let her go."

But she wouldn't get into her father's car until Connie had talked her into it. Then Miss Louise, her strong jaw jutting out, stepped up to the father and said sternly:

"Now don't you beat that child when you get her home. I'm going to ask her tomorrow, and if you've hurt her I'll see that

174

they put you where the dogs won't bark at you for a while."

"Oh, no'm, I wouldn't hurt her for nothin'," he protested.

It was a mournful dinner we ate that night. And again, Connie and I lay awake trying to figure this thing out. I kept insisting that it was a problem for which no solution existed in our society, but Connie maintained that we had to find a way.

When the girls came home from school the next day, they reported that Joanne had weathered the night and was going home again, trusting in Connie to help her. The little girls put down their books and lunch boxes and headed out again.

"Where are you going?" I asked.

"Oh," said Claire casually, "we're goin' to find a home for Joanne."

"Jes' like for kittens or doggies," Janie said.

"'Cept this time, we got somethin' even gooder to give away," Claire explained.

"Yeah," chorused Janie. "A chil'."

"Well, be back in time for supper," I told them gravely.

They were back for supper, but there was not the usual air of triumph about them which marked their normally successful efforts at salesmanship.

"Everybody says they got too many children now," Janie said sadly.

"But we found somebody wants a cat, Mommy. We got any cats to give away?"

"We can try again tomorrow, can't we, Claire? After church school."

"Yes," I said. "You try again tomorrow."

We were not surprised to see our pastor's car arrive at our place the following afternoon. He conducted weekly church school and often brought our girls home afterwards. Then,

Connie had written him a note about Joanne and she had hoped he would come to see us.

"I thought you'd be glad to hear the news," he said, as soon as he got into the house. "Joanne has found a new home."

Connie and I exchanged looks of surprise as he went on to say:

"And I think these little girls of yours deserve a lot of credit."

"Well, tell us what happened," I said.

"You know that your girls visited around, trying to find Joanne a home. Well, one of the people to whom they talked had some relatives who heard about the case. So, to make a long story short, they're going to take Joanne."

"It's Cordia's aunt," Cynthia explained.

"Oh, Mommy, isn't it wonderful?" Lynn squealed.

"Are they going to keep her?" Connie asked.

"Yes," the minister said. "They're a childless couple. Joanne's father says he'll give them permission to adopt her."

"Gosh, it all sounds too good to be true," I said, putting my arms around the little girls. "I just didn't believe that things like this happened."

We sat in silence for a few seconds. Then the minister spoke:

"I wonder if we could say a little prayer of thanks. I just can't help feeling God's hand in this."

As we bowed our heads, I stole a glance at the little girls. Their cheeks were radiant and their eyes were shining. They looked like a couple of small angels, at that.

Chapter 17

O U R family was dedicated to the proposition that every day was a holiday.

It might therefore be supposed that the normal holidays which are celebrated by mundane people would pass unnoticed. But our children were alert to this danger. They saw to it that we did not overlook the approach of a birthday or any of the super-holidays which are marked on calendars.

There were enough of us around so that we could celebrate a birthday almost every month. We allowed the children to choose the menu for their own birthday dinners. When Lynn's birthday came, she chose fried chicken as her treat. When Janie's big day came, she said:

"I wan' hot dogs, peas, noodles and mustachio ice cream."

Claire's tastes were just as plebeian.

"Kin we have hamboogers and buzzghetti, Mommy?" she asked on her birthday.

Larry explained that he was not so much interested in what food he had as he was in the color scheme. Each year, he specified that his cake and ice cream must be of a different color. One year, everything would have to be silver, another year it would be gold or blue. This year, he decided, the motif was to be red, white and blue—and he left it to Connie to work out the details.

So that everything between the children would be exactly even, we decided to spend the same amount of money on presents for each birthday. When the little girls couldn't make up their minds what they wanted for their birthdays, we decided to give them cash. Janie, being her father's daughter, tucked her money away in Connie's jewel box until she could decide what she really wanted. But whenever she found anything she thought she wanted, she would fall into agonies of indecision as to whether this was really the thing that she would most like to have. She made herself miserable for months, hoarding the money.

Claire, being the true daughter of her mother, talked Connie into taking her to Leonardtown the day after her birthday. She spent a happy hour in a toy store and came home loaded with junk which was forgotten in a week. She was flat broke again and completely happy.

Jack didn't approve of all of this fuss about birthdays, because of his allergy to holidays of any sort. Each birthday was a new horror to him. He would eat only two pieces of cake, instead of his normal four. He would protest that the children were being ruined with all the expensive presents they were getting. And then, when no one was looking, he would get down on the floor to see how the new toys worked.

He kept the date of his own birth a darkly guarded secret lest we try to stage some celebration for him. One day, Lynn managed to get a look at his driver's permit, which listed his birthday. We decided to surprise him with a party and some

178

presents. But the day before the party, he let us know that he had gotten wind of the scheme.

"That was just a phony date I gave to get my permit a few months early," he told Lynn, and roared with laughter.

She was quite upset by this news, but I took it calmly.

"It's probably his birthday, all right," I assured Connie. "But, if it's the wrong day, we'll give him a Humpty-Dumpty party."

We hocked the family silver and bought enough meat to serve Jack his favorite dish—swiss steak. Connie brought in a cake which said: "Happy Un-Birthday, Jack," as the rest of us sat around the table, chorusing one of his favorite singing commercials which was set to the tune of "Happy Birthday." We explained to him that the presents were all un-birthday gifts and that he should not feel unhappy. The party was a great success. It was the only holiday that we ever saw him really enjoy.

Eventually, Connie and I came to share some of Jack's antipathy for certain festive occasions. This was after school had started and we had learned what it was like not to have five children around the house all day long. School holidays in the county seemed to come early and often. Through some mysterious arrangement between the school board and the weather bureau, holidays occurred during a spell of bad weather. We would find ourselves cooped up in the house with our children and whatever host of friends they could assemble.

The first of these long holidays to fall after school had opened was at Hallowe'en. It was announced as a three-day affair—not because of Hallowe'en, but because there was a state-wide teachers' meeting.

"The teachers are pretty smart at that," I conceded. "Comes Hallowe'en and they scram clear out of the county."

"Too bad we can't have a state-wide parents' meeting," Connie said.

On Hallowe'en, there was a lot of scurrying around our house as the children put together their costumes. They were going to make their annual trick-or-treat tour of the neighborhood and we gave the little girls permission to go with them. I said that I would drive around and find them when it was bedtime for Janie and Claire.

Before they left the house, I gave them a stern warning against carrying their Hallowe'en pranks too far. As a boy, I had been well known locally as a member of a gang of young miscreants who were all wanted, dead or alive, by every farmer and storekeeper in the county. My wild reputation had outlived the days of my youth and there were still people who referred to me as "that bad boy." I was trying to make sure that my children did not follow in their father's footsteps.

"Be especially careful around Miss Annie's place," I said, referring to the odd character whom Connie had mistaken for a man that night. "You know what a crank she is."

They agreed to be prudent and set off happily. Shortly after eight o'clock, I drove down the road to round them up. I poked along the back roads for a time, without finding them. Suddenly, I spotted a figure that looked like Lynn, who had dressed as a witch. She was walking in the center of the road, waving a broomstick wildly.

I decided to have a little fun with the kids, so I slipped the car out of gear, dimmed my lights and coasted up behind the witch. When I got close, I let loose with a blast on my horn. The figure went straight up in the air, as if the broom was jet-equipped, and when it came down it was running. I sat there, roaring with laughter for a minute. Then I heard the children's voices down

180

the road, switched my lights on and drove down to pick them up.

To my surprise, Lynn was with them and I concluded guiltily that I had scared someone else's child.

"Have fun?" I asked.

They were bubbling with stories of their adventures.

"Any trouble?" I managed to ask at last.

"Just Miss Annie," Larry replied. "We were walking by her house, not doing anything, and she came out and chased us. That was just before you picked us up. Gosh, were we glad to see you!"

The next morning, I watched as Connie drove out of our road to the store. Then I saw her stop the car and talk to someone who was gesturing wildly. I recognized it as Miss Annie. Connie sat there listening for perhaps fifteen minutes, and finally drove off.

When she came home, I asked her about Miss Annie.

"Did the kids get in trouble with her?"

"Not the kids," Connie said. "It was 'that bad boy' she was giving me the lecture about. She says you sneaked up behind her and scared the daylights out of her with your car."

"Who, me?" I demanded.

"Yes, you. Next Hallowe'en, I'll let the kids go out—but you're going to stay home."

As Thanksgiving approached, I noticed that Jack was paying a great deal of attention to One Eye Connelly, the last survivor of our turkey flock.

"Think Connelly's going to be ready for Thanksgiving dinner?" I inquired of Jack at dinner one night.

"Mal de plume," he assured me.

The girls looked at me with horror.

181

"What's the matter?" I demanded. "That's what we raised him for."

"Oh, Daddy," Lynn protested. "If you killed poor Connelly, we wouldn't have anything to be thankful for."

"I think it's very unpolite to kill that poor turkey," Janie said.

"Well, what should we have for Thanksgiving dinner? Hot dogs?"

"I think turkey would be gooder 'an frankfooters," Claire observed. " 'Cept I don't think you should kill poor Connelly."

The Society for the Protection of One Eye Connelly went into action and I was backed into a corner and forced to promise him a long life. When I went by his pen the next time, the girls were feeding him my favorite pumpernickel bread and he gobbled at me derisively.

"Ok, I can't eat you," I muttered, "but I'll be darned if I'll keep you around here to laugh at me."

The next day, I sold him to a farmer who wanted a breeding tom for the following spring. I went to the store and bought another turkey for our dinner. Maybe it wasn't as big as Connelly, and maybe it hadn't been fattened on pumpernickel and hot biscuits, but at least it had two eyes.

With Thanksgiving out of the way, the children began the build-up for Christmas. Since it was to be our family's first Christmas together, we attached a lot of importance to it. For weeks, everyone was scurrying around the house, trying to hide a hundred presents in the two or three closets which Dad had managed to include in the place. Connie ordered most of the things for the children from the mail-order catalogues and every day she came home from the store staggering with packages.

I couldn't get any good hints about what she wanted for herself, so I finally asked her.

182

"A Persian kitten," she answered brightly.

"Oh, no," I moaned. "Couldn't it be something except one more darn animal?"

"Well, you asked me what I *wanted*," she said in a small voice.

"But Honey, be practical," I said.

"Okay, get me some double sheets," she said, with the air of a martyr.

"Now you're being silly. Either it's too practical or too impractical. Why can't you hit a happy medium?"

"Like for instance?"

"Oh, I don't know. Pretty clothes or something like that."

"Well, what do you want?"

"A garden tractor," I replied without hesitating.

"That you call practical?"

"What could be more practical, in an impractical way?"

"Maybe," she said slowly, "we'd better start all over."

"Okay. I'd like a warm sweater."

"And I'd love a nice dress."

I could see that Connie had her heart set on the kitten. But I felt about another pet just the way I knew she felt about anything for the farm—it would be just one more darn thing.

So I fought down my impulse to get the kitten and ordered a dress by mail for Connie from the New York department store, Lord and Taylor. This out of the way, I began to fret. After all, I told myself, to be unselfish in giving was the true spirit of Christmas. The kitten would be a true gift of the Magi. And so, cloaking my actions in more secrecy than an undercover man, I bought a Persian kitten and made arrangements to have it delivered to my family's home in Washington the day before Christmas.

Jack went home for Christmas, but my folks were coming

down to spend the afternoon. I chopped down three trees on Christmas Eve before I could get one that was small enough to go through the door. Connie and I stayed up until all hours decorating it, and then the children got us up before daylight.

I doled out presents amid wild squeals of joy and watched with horror as the individual piles of toys mounted.

"Either we'll have to throw out your old toys or move," I said.

"We could send our old toys to the poor kids in Italy," Lynn suggested.

Everyone chorused agreement to this.

"Fact," Janie said. "I think I'll give 'em some of 'at birfday money I can't amember to spend."

Finally, I came to the box which held Connie's dress and presented it to her as if it were just the thing she wanted, but didn't expect to get. Then she handed me my sweater. Each of us exclaimed happily over these very practical gifts and then shot envious glances at the children—who apparently had received everything they wanted, practical or not.

Connie went to the bedroom to slip into her new dress. When she came out again, I exclaimed in my best Phil Harris manner:

"Well, Lord and Taylor! Look at Mommy."

I saw a frown crease Cynthia's brow and a few minutes later, I heard her ask Connie:

"Mommy, why didn't Daddy like your new dress?"

"What makes you think he didn't like it?" Connie asked.

" 'Cause he swore when he saw you put it on," she said, looking worried as usual. "He said 'Lord, the tailor!' "

I sat for a time, admiring my new sweater and thinking how nice it would look on a man who was operating his own garden tractor. I saw Connie trailing a piece of string across the floor, as if she had a kitten to chase it. It was about this time that I heard a clatter on the lawn. I ran to the window and saw one of our neighbors puffing up the hill with a garden tractor.

"Is it mine?" I called wildly to Connie.

She nodded happily.

"I got them to hide it for me," she said. "Come on, let's see how it runs."

I put my arm around her waist and we rushed out. I was just about to set off and plow myself a furrow when Dad's car pulled into the yard. I rushed over, burrowed in the back seat where my sister sat and came up with a fuzzy, silver-gray Persian kitten.

After I handed it to Connie, she was so overcome with joy that tears rolled down her cheeks and she couldn't talk.

We had a joyful Christmas dinner. There were ten of us at the long table and we filled up on turkey and plum pudding. After the dishes had been done, everyone made a dive for his favorite present. Even Dad was in a mellow, relaxed mood. Instead of getting into his work clothes and tearing out a partition somewhere, he just strolled around the place humming and making mental notes for future demolition projects.

Some time later, I heard my mother ask Lynn:

"Is that your father I hear out there running the new tractor?"

"No," Lynn replied. "That's Mommy running the tractor. Daddy's in the bedroom playing with the kitten."

Chapter 18

WE had started from scratch in our effort to build up a homestead that would yield all of the necessities of family life except possibly bubble gum and sirloin steaks. After six months, we were still scratching.

I had a flock of hens which produced plenty of eggs for the table. We had put a number of fryers in the freezer. Our original two goats had multiplied to five. Phyllis, after refusing to give any milk at first, made a come back. She and Prudence were producing between five and six quarts of milk a day between them.

"The milk we get from the goats," I told Connie triumphantly one day, "isn't costing us any more than buying it at the store."

She greeted this statement with skepticism. Having seen the steady parade of veterinarians who had come to treat Phyllis' ills and having watched me digging down into my pocket every week to pay for feed, fencing and milking equipment, Connie was convinced that we could buy champagne for less than the goat's milk was costing us.

"Just wait until next year when I'll have four goats milking,"

I said. "We'll have butter and cheese, too. That'll really save some money."

"But do you think we can afford to save that much?" she asked. "We're nearly in the poorhouse now, with what we've been saving on milk alone."

This question of how much various items of free produce were actually costing was being raised more and more often by Connie. One night, she reached into the freezer and came up with some of the previous summer's string beans and strawberries.

"Oh, boy," Claire cried when dinner was served. "Are these scream beans out of our own garden, Daddy?"

"Yup," I replied proudly. "We're beginning to live off the land now. These beans didn't cost us a cent."

"How about the seed?" Connie asked.

"Twenty cents," I said. "Why you couldn't even buy one quart of frozen beans for that."

"What about the freezer? Don't you include that?"

"Okay. These beans, children, cost us $350.20, which is rather high for beans. But the next box will be absolutely free."

"And what about the garden tractor?" Connie demanded.

"I guess we'll have to charge that against the next box of beans," I admitted. "Children, to show you how you can save money by mass production, the next box of beans will cost only two hundred twenty dollars. After that they're free."

"If we don't have to buy some more equipment," Connie added.

"I think it's nice of Daddy to support our food," Claire said. "Specially, for it costs so much."

"Is this meat out of our own garden, too, Daddy?" asked Cynthia.

"No," I said contemptuously. "This is store meat. Round steak."

"Humph," Cynthia replied. "Tastes like beef to me."

"What animal does it come off, Daddy?" asked Claire.

"A cow," I said.

"This is not a very pleasant conversation," Lynn protested. "I don't like to think about a poor cow getting killed while I'm eating it."

"What's for bezerk?" Janie demanded.

"Berries," Connie replied.

"Oh, boy," Janie cried. "Struggleberries?"

Connie nodded.

"My gosh, Daddy, why don't you teach these little brats how to speak English," Larry demanded. "You need an interpreter around here. For bezerk we're having struggleberries! "

"Well, Larry, 'at 's what Daddy said they were," Janie insisted.

"When did he ever say that?" said Larry derisively.

"I heard him las' summer. He said, 'Golly but it's a struggle to raise 'ese berries.' "

"Well," I said when order was restored, "at least, the berries are free. Thank Heaven, we paid for the freezer when we ate the main course."

As a result of Connie's teasing, I began to keep records on my farm costs. I finally concluded that my dream of the Pioneer Family, tilling the soil and supporting itself, was better suited for some other century. This was the age of commerce, I had to admit. And to buy the things that were needed to assure a family food supply, I was going to have to sell some things.

My expenses were particularly heavy because I was just starting out and I had to buy all kinds of equipment. I needed

188

Jack to help me clear land and put up buildings. Even the small sum I paid him in cash wages was an expense that couldn't be covered by a little food for our table. And I still had to count the bill from the auto accident as part of his wage. So I began to calculate the items that I could raise for retail sale. Eggs, chickens and whatever other poultry I could raise looked like the surest way to build up a small cash income from the place. So we went into business on a modest scale, trying to cover expenses.

This began to work out. I sold enough eggs to cover the cost of the hens, including eggs for the family. By selling half of a crop of frying chickens, I found I could pay the expenses of putting the other half away for ourselves.

Dad shook his head and chuckled at my efforts. We were in the store one day when the members of a baseball team sponsored by a local business man came in. Across the back of their uniforms was the lettering: "Chr. Heurich Brewers."

"I can just see it now," Dad laughed, sweeping his hand out. "One day I'll be here and in they'll come in their nice new uniforms. On the back, it'll say: 'Alfred Toombs, Fresh Eggs.'"

But Connie took little joy in my egg and poultry business. The only thing she approved of was my sale of one of the goat kids for ten dollars. I wouldn't let her have a frying chicken for the house until I had sold enough to pay the feed bill. And when eggs got scare, the family had to live on what were left after I took care of the cash customers.

As a gesture of protest against this new policy, Connie bought a dozen eggs at the store one day when we ran short.

"Got 'em five cents a dozen cheaper than yours, too," she crowed.

As the winter waned, Jack and I began to make preparations

189

for the season ahead. Since I had a considerable investment in Jack, I was determined to get as much work out of him as I could.

The goats ate down the honeysuckle and weeds and Jack went behind them uprooting trees. Then we got a farmer to come in and do the heavy plowing for us. We planted a pasture for the goats; sowed soy beans in the orchard and made a run for poultry; added to the barn and chicken house and built a warm brooder house to start young poultry in the spring. Then we began getting the ground in shape for the sort of super garden that would yield a year's supply of vegetables.

When Jack was in the proper mood for work, it was necessary to find out first what sort of thing he was allergic to that day. If I had made plans to pour concrete in the barn and discovered that Jack was allergic to cement that day, we would have to work at digging the root cellar instead. If he was feeling allergic to tar, I would have to put roofing on by myself.

By the time we started getting the garden ready, I found I had a new problem with him. Jack was crazy about most vegetables, but there were certain kinds that he could not stand. He insisted upon knowing, as we went along in the garden, just what was going to be planted in each area.

"I'm going to put peas in here," I would say.

"Boy, I love fresh peas," he would answer with enthusiasm.

Immediately, he would start the garden tractor and plow up the area in a storm. He would work manure into the ground and leave it as smooth as a putting green.

One day, as we started to work on a plot of ground, he asked:

"Whatcha gonna plant here, Doc?"

"Green peppers," I replied.

"Ugh, I can't stand 'em. What goes next to 'em?"

"Cucumbers," I told him.

"How repulsible," he said. "You're not going to waste good manure on stuff like that, are you?"

We walked back up to the house. Connie asked Jack to take a basket of old papers and magazines down to burn and I returned to my typewriter. A short time later, I glanced out of the window to see how Jack was getting on. I saw him sitting on the ground next to the incinerator, reading some of the kids' old comic books and, as he finished one, dropping it on the fire. It took him two hours to burn the trash.

When he finally got around to working on the ground for the peppers and cucumbers, he did such a poor job that I had to go over it myself.

There was one little corner of the new garden which the plowman had not been able to touch. It was going to be a tough job to clean it out by hand and before I mentioned the subject to Jack, I wanted to be sure that his approach to it was going to be eager.

"Do you like watermelons, Jack?" I asked, figuring that this was a safe bet.

"They're disgustipatin'," he said, making a face.

This news staggered me. I regard watermelons very highly, personally, and I was certain that this spot was ideal for them. I looked so surprised at his answer that he asked:

"Why?"

"Oh, I was just wondering," I said.

"What I like best is tomatoes. I can gobble 'em by the bushel."

"Well, this looks like a good place for tomatoes," I said, pointing to the piece of rough ground.

"Okay, Doc, right away. Mighty astutable."

Jack worked like a machine and, when he had finished, I took him to another part of the garden and convinced him that it was even better land for tomatoes.

"Okay. I'll go to work on it," he said cheerfully. "But whatcha aim to plant down that other place?"

"Watermelons," I replied.

Jack referred constantly to the book on homesteading which had touched me off in the first place. He was always finding fresh ideas for projects and when he mentioned one, Connie would hoot and want to know how much it was going to cost. We would assure her that we were going to get double our money back and would order blueberries, raspberries, boysenberries, asparagus or a few more dwarf fruit trees.

I had a couple of rhubarb plants; however, Jack didn't think that these were sufficient. He wanted me to order more, but I resolutely refused until I could get one little detail straightened out with Connie.

"Why is it?" I asked her, "that you always serve rhubarb the same way? All we ever get is rhubarb pie. Why don't you fix it differently sometimes?"

"That's the only recipe for it I can find," she said.

I got down the cook book, thumbed through the index and found a dozen recipes listed under rhubarb.

"That's funny," she said. "I've looked in there I don't know how many times and I couldn't even find the word. All I could find was under 'pie, rhubarb.'"

I looked at her curiously for a minute.

"How do you spell the word, Dear?" I asked, recalling that she spelled strictly by ear.

"R-u-b-a-r-b," she said.

"Next time, look under r-*h*-u-b-a-r-b," I said. Then I turned to Jack: "Okay, we'll buy a couple more roots, now that we've got that straightened out."

One day, Jack and I stood on the bank of the little inlet that leads from the river into our creek. We watched a couple of neighbor boys tonging up oysters. Several weeks later I learned that, since I had riparian rights to the stream, those oysters really belonged to me. When Jack found out about this, he got excited.

"Nothin' to do now but buy some seed oysters and put 'em down there," he said. "There's a whole new crop we'll have."

He nagged me until I finally invested more money in oysters. They had the virtue, I was told, of requiring absolutely no care. All you had to do was wait a couple of years and then take them up. But Jack didn't hold with this theory. When I had any particularly hard job for him to do, he would always disappear in the direction of the oyster bed. He would wade around, inspecting the oysters and, I supposed, counting them.

He came back from one of these sessions one day and asked me:

"Do you ever do things and then wonder why you did them?"

"It seems to me that you've put that same problem to me before," I replied. "What fool thing have you done now?"

"I was wonderin' why I had put on my best shoes to go wading around in the creek."

"Well, why did you?" I asked.

"Because my other shoes were wet!" he said, and laughed happily.

But I didn't know what trouble was until I allowed Jack to talk me into becoming a bee keeper. I ordered the bee hive and the bees early in the winter, for delivery in the spring.

The bee hive came almost immediately and I wondered why it was sent so far ahead of the date when the bees were promised. When I came to assemble the hive, I discovered why. For the hive consisted of several hundred small pieces of wood, wire and wax. Maybe the bees knew how to put it together, but I didn't.

The pieces arrived in three separate packages, over a period of ten days, and I was never absolutely sure that all of it had reached me. In the last package came the directions. They had been written, I was convinced, by a Mongolian idiot who had never seen a bee. They told me absolutely nothing about what I was to do with the several hundred assorted pieces.

We stacked the parts of the bee hive in a corner of the living room and in the evenings, as we watched television, we took turns trying to put it together. We didn't get far and concluded that it was because we weren't very bright. But then we began to try it out on all our visitors, as if it were a jigsaw puzzle. Finally, we got two layers of the hive put together and Connie said:

"We're leading the simple life and that will have to be good enough for our bees, too."

When the bees themselves arrived, I put them in the hive and much to the consternation of my family I didn't get stung at all. But a few weeks later, I realized that I was really stung. The bees scrammed out, leaving me holding a bill for thirty dollars' worth of equipment, and set up housekeeping elsewhere.

Jack was always finding an advertisement for a new kind of poultry that he thought we should try. I would order some chickens which were supposed to have a lot of white meat and then he'd insist that I try another breed that had a lot of dark meat. He talked me into entering a contest where you explained in five hundred words or less why you liked a certain breed of chickens. To everyone's surprise, I won second prize.

"What do you get for your prize?" Connie asked.

"Fifty more chickens," I said with delight.

"Oh, well," she observed. "Don't feel bad. We can't all be lucky."

Having stocked up now on all leading brands of chickens, Jack persuaded me to try ducks. Much against my better judgment, I ordered twenty-five ducklings and sat back to wait for the trouble to begin.

A few days after the ducks arrived and were ensconced in their brooder, we had to take the children to town overnight. We left Jack in charge of the establishment and put enough food in the ice box to feed the First United States Army.

"There's a five-gallon container of ice cream in the freezer, if you want any," Connie said as we left.

When we got back, the food in the ice box was untouched. But there was almost nothing left of the ice cream.

"What did you do, live on ice cream for thirty-six hours?" I asked.

"That was all I wanted," he said laconically.

"Did you eat ice cream for breakfast, too?" Larry demanded enviously.

"Sure, put it on my cornflakes," he replied.

"How's everything around the farm?" I asked.

"Oh, just as verdamp as usual. Except we ain't keepin' ducks any more."

"Why not?" I demanded.

"They left."

"What are you talking about?"

"They got out of the brooder las' night. Mal de plume. I spent all day lookin' for them, but I could only find one."

"Only one out of the whole bunch?"

"Yeah. And that was dead."

"Well, that beats me. I knew ducks were a poor idea."

"When you gonna get some more?" he demanded.

"No more ducks," I said stoutly. "In fact, no more nothin'. We've got more than we can look after now. I should have quit just before I got that bee hive. That's when my luck changed. This sort of thing can get expensive."

Jack could see that I meant it this time and he looked truly crestfallen. He went to bed early and, just before I decided to turn in myself, I walked out on the front porch. It was a cold, rainy night and the wind was whistling through the pine trees. But suddenly, I heard a sound that was familiar—the ducks chirping.

My eyes fell on a spot where a shaft of light from the house was hitting the ground. There, huddled together in a mud puddle, were the little yellow ducks. I was overjoyed as I gathered them up and put them back in the warmth of the brooder.

"I don't see how they ever lived," I told Jack the next day. "No other bird could have survived that."

"See what I told you about ducks," he cried triumphantly. "They're astutable. Now will you change your mind and buy something else?"

"Like what?"

"Like turkeys, for an instance."

Jack had touched me on a tender point there. I had made

196

such a miserable flop of raising turkeys the summer before that it had made me mad. First, I swore I would never have another and then, getting obstinate, I had said I would raise twice as many the next year, just to prove that I could do it. I was willing to forget the latter oath, but Jack wasn't going to let me.

One of the country's most successful turkey men lives in our county. He is Hobart Norman, a tense lanky man with thinning hair and a faintly worried expression—from raising turkeys. I spent a lot of time that winter talking to him and learned a lot of things about raising turkeys that I hadn't known when I started out so confidently, my little homesteading book in hand, the summer before.

The turkey is a notoriously stupid fowl which shows a real talent for only one thing—suicide. Norman went into some detail to explain to me most of the ingenious ways which turkeys employ to destroy themselves. Having completed my course of instruction from him, I bought twenty-five day-old poults. They cost eighty-five cents each—or about as much as an eight-weeks-old broiling chicken.

As we put them into the brooder house, where the temperature was adjusted to exactly ninety-five degrees, we had to teach them to eat and drink by dipping each bird's beak into feed and water. For the first few days, we had to check each bird to make sure that he wasn't pulling a fast one and starving himself to death. We scattered marbles and bright stones on their feed to fool them into eating. They will peck at shiny objects of this kind, and unwittingly pick up some feed in the process.

I made up my mind that these turkeys were going to yield me a profit. When, after four weeks of babying them, I noted

197

that I had only lost two of the birds, I began to feel a measure of success.

"By the time they were four weeks old last year," I told Connie, "I had lost half of them."

"But how much longer do you have to go?" she asked.

"Oh, about five months. You can kill them when they're twenty-eight weeks old."

"They'll find some way to cost you a fortune before then, don't worry," she assured me cheerfully.

I insisted upon hospital-like sanitary precautions around the turkeys, since they are prey to almost every known disease. Before we fed them, we scrubbed like surgeons. We dipped our shoes in disinfectant before stepping into their pen. Connie protested against being subjected to such a routine, but she was crazy about the foolish little birds and would follow our rules so that she could feed them. We wouldn't let the children go into the brooder house. They had to look at the turkeys through glass.

"Those birds might learn bad manners from you chillun, or catch the sniffles or turkeypox or somethin'," Jack would say.

In spite of Connie's dire forecast, the birds grew and disaster didn't overtake them. When other things went wrong around the farm, I would cheer myself by figuring up the profits which I stood to make on the turkeys in the fall. But one day Connie came to me and said quietly:

"I was just out feeding your turkeys."

"Have fun?" I asked cheerfully.

"You were right," she said. "You should have quit before you got the bees. At least, before you got turkeys."

"What are you talking about? The turkeys are one thing I stand to show a real profit on."

198

"Not any more," she said.

I looked at her with alarm.

"One of them just pecked the diamond out of my ring," she said timidly. "I was feeding them pumpernickel bread."

"Which one was it?" I moaned.

"How would I know?" she said. "All turkeys look alike to me."

"I can't kill them all," I told her. "They'll be worth more than the diamond."

"Won't the diamond get lost?"

"Maybe. But probably it'll wind up in the gizzard."

"What's the gizzard?"

"It's a little sack-like business where they collect stones. That's how they chew their food. We'll find it maybe when we kill the birds."

"Or somebody will get a diamond in their giblet gravy," she said sadly.

"Gee, I just can't win," I said, shaking my head slowly and walking toward the turkeys. "Somewhere out there stands the most expensive turkey in America."

Chapter 19

A S the months passed, the scars left by my two-year hitch as a housekeeper began to heal. I slipped back easily into the role of the man of the house.

True, I still fixed breakfast every morning. Occasionally, someone would clamor for me to cook a cheese soufflé for dinner, or fry fish and hush puppies or to whip up some hollandaise sauce. But these were occasional contributions, and they stirred no memories of the deadly monotonous routine of regular housekeeping.

Forgotten, too, were the vows I had once made that no wife of mine would ever have to work the housekeepers' 144-hour, seven-day week without any relief from me. I was now obsessed with the problems of building a retaining wall for the barn or with sorting out ideas for a new magazine article. I never gave a thought to how many beds there were to make every day nor how hard it was to think of a different dessert for dinner every night.

I played the part of housekeeper emeritus, always ready with some good sound advice for my successor. I would sample the crab gumbo knowingly and suggest to Connie that it could do with a little more *file*. Or I would cluck disapprovingly when I saw her commit some sacrilege such as washing my cast-iron pancake griddle with soap and water. I could tell from the looks she gave me in return that this was not entirely the sort of housekeeping help she had expected from me. In fact, she sometimes got a little rebellious.

There was the matter of the potato peels. I owned a perfectly good patented potato peeler which would take the skin off a spud so thin that you could see daylight through it. But Connie scorned it, no matter how often I pressed it upon her. She insisted upon doing it her own way, which was with a dull knife. Jack, seeing the thickness of the potato peels she was throwing out, spread them around on the garden.

One day, he walked into the kitchen eating a small, raw potato.

"Hey Connie, I got me a whole potato patch from those peelin's you throw out," he said, and gave me a broad wink.

"Well," she said. "It's a good thing I didn't use Al's potato peeler. You boys won't have to buy any seed potatoes, now."

But I couldn't hold my place as a reserve cook forever. Connie came down with the flu one day and I was called back into active service. It seemed to me that here was the opportunity to demonstrate personally how efficiently and economically the household could actually be operated.

For the first two days, I ran the house as smoothly as if I had been born with dishpan hands. The contrast between my methods and Connie's became immediately apparent, although I am not sure that they entirely demonstrated the superiority of either. Unless threatened with a knife, Connie wouldn't fry anything. When I started cooking again, I fried everything except the spinach. She made her gingerbread in a few minutes with a prepared mix from the store. I spent an hour fixing an old-fashioned gingercake with a black-strap molasses base. Connie had to nag the children to do their chores around the house. I merely let out a couple of roars and they worked like the devil himself was after them.

But on the third morning at my new job, I began to experience that old dizzy feeling. After I got the children off to school with waffles and sausage under their belts, I took a look around the kitchen and then leaned against the wall to support myself. There, on the table and sticky with syrup, were the same 250,000 dishes which I had washed the night before. And the noon before. And the morning before. The kitchen, which I had left so spotless before I went to bed, was littered now with paper napkins, corn flakes and a pair of girl's pajamas. The cats and dogs were yowling for their breakfast, the garbage pail hadn't been emptied and I had forgotten to buy coffee at the store. And then I couldn't think of anything to have for dessert that evening.

I went in to take Connie's temperature.

"Just wanted to see how long before you'd be up again," I said glumly.

Jack would hang around the kitchen in the morning, waiting for me to outline his work orders for the day. He did not like to labor alone and so he stalled around the house as much as possible. There was nearly always a wide, dirty circle in the living room where I had swept around him. Sometimes, he would pitch in wildly and help with the housework, but I couldn't count on it. Usually, he would simply get up from the table, leaving his dishes where they lay, and say:

"Reckon I'll see what's on the televisionary set."

202

Then he would sit down for an hour and watch a wild-west movie while I scrubbed the kitchen floor, dunked that pile of dishes and rolled out a pie crust. Occasionally, he would move the TV set to another spot.

"What do you do that for?" I asked.

"Durn movies are always the same," he explained. "If I move the set around, I can look at 'em from a different angle."

It wasn't long before I began to understand better what Connie had been up against in feeding Dad and Jack. We had meals at regular hours now. But Dad would never eat on the same schedule with the rest of us. He sometimes would get up at 6 A. M. and when I got to the kitchen, I was faced with the remnants of his breakfast. Other days, he stayed in bed until ten o'clock and took his breakfast after I had cleaned up the kitchen following the first shift. Under either circumstance, he would always have to eat lunch earlier or later than the rest of the family.

When dinner time came, Dad would be up in an apple tree spraying or under the house giving his plumbing its weekly repairs. That would mean keeping his meal warm for fifteen minutes after the others were served. He suffered from migraine headaches and when he had one, he would fast. So you could never tell whether he was even coming to the table at all.

Jack was never late for meals. In fact, he was generally early. As soon as lunch was over, he would be ready for dinner. One night, after he had polished off several family-sized helpings at dinner, I saw him start dragging out the makings for one of his incredible sandwiches.

"Eatin' always makes me hungry," he explained.

Jack neither smoked, drank nor swore. In fact, he did not even drink coffee. But while Connie was sick, he suddenly fell into a sleepless period and would always be getting up before daybreak. One morning, he asked me for a cup of coffee. Then he asked for a refill.

"Trying to break the habit," he said. "Tapering off with just two cups today."

By a little skillful questioning, I learned that he had gotten up early one morning and made a pot of coffee for Connie and me. He decided to sample it and finally drank the whole pot. Since then, he had been drinking six cups of coffee before breakfast every day.

"Think that's what gave me the imblesomnia?" he asked.

When I noted the quantities of food required to keep Jack afloat, I understood why Connie was having trouble staying within her budget. In fact, I ran five dollars over the allowance the first week and had to ask her to write the household check a day early. To have heard her, you would have thought I was asking for two quarts of blood.

"My gosh, it's only money," I protested. "You're making more noise than I do when this happens to you."

"That's just it," she replied. "I am not."

Going into the second week, I was naturally determined to save that five dollars back. My first official money-saving act was to eliminate cream cheese and olives from our diet and get us back on a bologna sandwich standard of lunch. I managed to save the five dollars by a lot of niggardly tricks that I had learned as a housekeeper. But Connie suffered fifteen dollars' worth when I fed her peanut-butter sandwiches instead of fruit salad for her lunches.

After three weeks of running the house, working on the farm and trying to earn enough at the typewriter to pay for both, I was getting a little ragged around the edges. Somehow, the housekeeping wasn't the happy little part-time job it had been for the first couple of days. The corners didn't always get swept and the beds weren't always made. I found myself buying ready-mixed biscuits and serving stew twice in the same week. The first time Connie felt well enough to get up and wash the breakfast dishes, I bowed three times in the direction of Mecca.

I was a chastened man by the time she was able, with all my sympathies, to take over the housekeeping again. I would be filled with pity after that when I saw her struggling with a sink full of dishes or faced with the mess left on the table after lunch. In fact, I felt so sorry for her that I even helped her out, sometimes.

It was about this time that my income tax came due. I discovered to my horror that I owed the Government seven hundred dollars more than I had on hand. So I had to float a quick loan to see me through. This, of course, launched me on a violent new crusade for economy.

"Do you realize what this means?" I roared around the house. "I've spent seven hundred dollars more than I earned."

Connie seemed unimpressed.

"How do you figure that?" she asked calmly. "You borrowed the seven hundred dollars, didn't you?"

"Sure, I borrowed it. But what's that got to do with it? It's spent."

"But how can you say you spent it?" she demanded triumphantly. "You still owe it!"

"This way lies madness," I muttered and dropped the subject.

A few days later, I cashed Connie's weekly household check at the bank and was driving home when I passed a grocery store. A sign in the window said: "Going Out of Business—All Merchandise At Cost." I slammed on my brakes and a few minutes later was busily rummaging through the store. Everything was going at half price, or less, and so I loaded up on canned milk, frozen foods, soaps and canned goods. At half price, even olives and cream cheese looked cheap so I bought some.

When I got home, I staggered in with my burden and announced triumphantly:

"Boy, did I save you a lot of money today! I spent thirty dollars and got sixty dollars' worth of groceries."

Connie merely looked dismayed.

"You spent thirty dollars on groceries?" she demanded. "It will take all my week's food budget to pay for that."

"Sure—but look at what you'll be saving for weeks ahead."

"But what am I going to do this week?" she asked again. Then she sighed and said: "Well, I suppose we can live out of the freezer until I can make up for this."

For a long time, Connie had been teasing me about getting fat. But now after my stint of cooking what I liked, she contended that I had gained ten pounds and shoved me on the scales to prove it. I was willing to shrug the whole thing away, but she was not.

I spent the next two weeks trying to avoid the subject entirely, but this effort netted me a loss of only one pound. When further resistance to her seemed hopeless, I agreed to start on a diet.

Now diets are horrible enough, at best, but the way Connie ran this one merely proved that it was something that the Chinese had not yet perfected when they introduced the water torture.

My bride was a good cook, of the no-nonsense school. She generally stuck to plain, easy-to-fix dishes which had lots of vitamins and not too many calories. But as soon as she got me on that diet, she began to practice spectacular rites in the kitchen which I had never seen before. The result was that instead of the baked chicken which might normally be served for Sunday dinner, she would come up with Maryland fried chicken or stewed chicken and dumplings. Cauliflower and cabbage, which normally were served with pristine plainness, now came out drenched in rich sauces.

When my diet would permit two ounces of boiled noodles at a meal, Connie would knock herself out to fix a casserole containing noodles, mushrooms, bits of bacon or walnuts, soaked in a white sauce and topped with baked cheese. I would sit staring at it moodily, trying to figure out how to separate the noodles from the calories and she would say:

"You look so hungry. Take some of the nice crispy part on top."

"But that's cheese," I would protest. "I'm just supposed to have noodles."

"But your diet allows you cheese."

"That was for lunch. I got one ounce of cheese with my lettuce and tomato salad with the, ugh, mineral oil dressing."

"Oh, shucks. And I put cheese on your apple pie tonight, too. . . . Why are you looking at me like that? I know that you're supposed to get an apple for dessert tonight."

"That's a baked apple."

"The pie's baked. You can just eat the apple part and leave the crust."

Not only Connie, but the children too developed an acute case of over-sympathy for me. Instead of gobbling down their

207

candy on the way home from school, the girls would get to the house with their sweets ration still intact. They would rush up and wave candy bars under my nose and if I refused to take a bite, their feelings would be hurt.

While I was in the depths of the diet, we began to have a lot of visitors who brought along boxes of candy or bottles of high-calory liquor. Old friends, from whom we had not heard in months, began to mail rare cheeses and fruit cakes from distant points. I never did figure out how the word got around so fast about my diet.

At this rate, of course, I went along for a couple of weeks and lost no weight at all. Finally, I decided that I couldn't stand the torture any longer.

"What are we having tonight?" I asked Connie.

"Broccoli," she replied. "And I fixed some hollandaise, because I know you must be getting tired of plain broccoli."

"What do you mean, tired of it? We haven't had it plain since I went on this diet."

"I'll be glad when the diet's over," she said, pouting a little. "Going hungry this way makes you so cross."

That did it. I gobbled down the hollandaise with a clear conscience and at bed time I drank the cocoa Connie fixed because she decided I must be getting tired of skimmed milk. When the kids shoved chocolates into my mouth, I ate them and I pitched into the box of candied fruit that Aunt Dorothy sent.

One night a few days later, I announced to the family:

"Okay, everybody. I'm back to my normal weight. The diet's all over."

There were shouts of joy from the children.

208

"Kin you eat whatever you want, now, Daddy?" Janie demanded.

"Yes, sir," I beamed happily.

Everyone lost interest in my condition immediately. The children managed to do away with all their gum drops before they got home. The only gift package that came in was a smoked herring. Connie stopped worrying about whether my food was monotonous. Chickens were baked again. Cabbage came off the stove boiled, period.

Conditions were ideal and I ate my way along carefully, so as not to attract any attention.

In the next month, I lost those extra ten pounds.

Chapter 20

T_O the great delight of our children, who were convinced that no two days should be alike, we had a fairly steady stream of visitors on Dukehart Island.

Our guests added a certain spice to life which would have been missing otherwise. They fixed things around the place that I was never able to repair, before they came or after they left. They brought us presents that we would never have thought of buying for ourselves—five pounds of Roquefort cheese, for instance.

Our friends always seemed to fall into one of two classifications: those who didn't come when they were expected and those who did come when they were not expected.

One of my friends managed to fall into both of these classifications in the space of a single month. We invited him down for three successive week ends, but he failed to appear. Connie was thoroughly annoyed, but I insisted upon offering a fourth invitation. My friend positively assured me that he couldn't make it, so we invited some other people instead. The house was filled to overflowing when my pal appeared and announced happily that he'd been able to make it, after all.

The children always took great delight in these unexpected circumstances. Whenever possible, they would do something unexpected themselves, just to add a little to the situation.

The most consistently unexpected visitor we had was our pastor. One rainy afternoon, not long after I married Connie, his car pulled into the yard. The children had been playing in the house all day and the place looked as if a small but violent tornado had paused briefly in the living room. Connie had been painting furniture and the pastor never having seen her before when her face was tinted robin's egg blue, did not immediately recognize her.

We invited him to stay for dinner and then it was that the children began to behave unexpectedly. About five-thirty, Cynthia popped into the living room and asked the minister:

"What sort of cocktail would you like?"

Just then, the little girls marched into the room singing one of the commercials they had learned from Jack:

"How mile, how mile, how mile kin a cig'ret be?"

Claire immediately jumped into our visitor's lap, ran her dirty little hands flirtatiously around his stiff white collar and started to chatter. Janie stood back and studied the minister curiously.

"Mommy doesn't b'lieve in your church," Janie said suddenly.

"Oh, you're mistaken, dear," Connie interposed quickly. "It's just that I used to attend Quaker Meetings in New York."

Operating on the theory that the sooner she got the children's mouths stuffed with food, the better off we'd all be, Connie rushed dinner on the table. As we sat down, I beamed proudly toward the minister and asked:

"Which of you children would like to say grace tonight?"

211

There was a moment of awkward silence and then Larry suggested happily:

"Let's shoot dice for it."

"Perhaps we should say grace Quaker style," Connie suggested quickly.

We bowed our heads and Janie said:

"Quack, quack."

"What are you doing?" I demanded a little sharply.

"Sayin' grace quacker style," she explained quite seriously.

"One week end, a cousin of the children—a boy of fourteen —came to visit. He surprised us by hinting that he would like iced tea with his lunch and by requesting coffee—which we didn't serve our children—with dinner. During the evening, he and Larry were playing with the electric train. I heard someone in the kitchen during the evening and fancied that I smelled the aroma of coffee brewing. When I looked in on them at bed time, I found the boys hauling half a dozen stained coffee cups on top of the cars. When I looked surprised, the cousin explained that he had drunk all the coffee—but that I shouldn't worry. He'd been a coffee drinker since he was six and was used to it. I guess he was, because he fell asleep like a tired puppy that night.

The house was usually full of little girls who were spending the night with one or the other of ours. By far the most intriguing of these were a pair of sisters who came to see the little girls. Although they apparently had full use of their vocal cords, they never spoke a word to me. I would say hello as they entered the house, and they would give me frozen little smiles. When I served their dinner, I would have to turn to Claire and say:

"Ask your little friends whether they would like to have gravy on their potatoes."

There would be a whispered conference at the other end of the table and Claire would reply:

"They say yes, but not too much."

Our grown-up guests fell into two classifications according to their sleeping habits, also. They either got up too early or slept too late. For the late sleepers, we had a remedy. We warned that the children would be bound and gagged until 10 A. M., but anyone who tried to sleep after that hour did so at his own peril.

But we never learned quite how to cope with the early risers. We would hear them in the kitchen at 6 A. M. on a Sunday morning, upsetting pots and pans as they tried to find out where we kept the makings for coffee. There is nothing quite so disconcerting as to stagger out to the kitchen early in the morning and to find someone there waiting for you to make coffee. There is a ten-minute pause ahead which is bound to strain the most cordial friendship.

One of our guests, who spent several days with us, suffered from early-morning insomnia. He would get up at dawn, down several cups of coffee he had brewed himself, and would be waiting for me as soon as I got out of bed. I was still groggy, but he was already in the mood for songs, dances and witty conversation. I finally suggested to Jack that he take this guest down to the barn at milking time and they had a fine time talking together by the dawn's early light.

Those who came to visit us were exposed to the sort of hazards which we had come to expect as routine in the country. There are no delicatessens in the country, which means that once the Sunday menu is set—and the stores are closed—the amount or type of food cannot be swiftly changed to meet circumstances.

We tried to cater to our guests' preference in food, but because of this inflexibility in the law of supply, we often had trouble. One Sunday, we had as our guest a friend of mine who had just come over from England. I had suggested that Connie fry chicken, country style. This was the only meat in the house that day when shortly before dinner my friend dropped the bit of information that he hoped to fill up on red meat while he was in America.

"I've eaten so much chicken over there in the last year that I've got pinfeathers," he said.

As time went on Connie became something of a magician because of the unexpected guests who arrived just before meal time. But there was one meal that even a magician couldn't have stretched.

We had a couple of friends in the house for the week end. Connie decided that one of our meaty ducks would make a nice meal. Jack had gone to town for the week end and Dad told us he wouldn't be down at all. Just before dinner on Sunday, Dad appeared and brought Jack with him. Connie still thought that we would be able to stretch the duck, if I garnished each plate with plenty of apple sauce. But as we sat down to dinner, some further reinforcements arrived and before we got under way, I found myself faced with the problem of dividing one fat duck among thirteen people.

I served everyone plenty of apple sauce, garnished with thin slices of duck. Jack got the neck and a piece of brown skin. To Dad, I awarded the parson's nose.

We finally concluded that the perfect guest, like a good man, is mighty hard to find now-a-days. Those who most nearly approached this status in our books were those who didn't take the matter of a little hospitality too seriously. The guests who

214

felt that they must immediately repay us twice over with goods or services left us a little unnerved.

My brother-in-law was one who was given to the grand gesture. One afternoon, we asked him to pick up a couple of quarts of ice cream for dinner. He came back from the store with five gallons of it. Our freezer was full to the lid with vegetables and that summer afternoon, five gallons of ice cream suddenly turned into quite a liability. As a little remembrance of his visit that time, he bought a dozen of the noisiest bantam chickens in the East and presented them to Lynn and Cynthia.

The proper care and training of house guests, Connie and I discovered, is a tricky job. One of our problems was to make sure that ours didn't get too helpful around the place.

There is no beaver so eager as a city man turned loose in the country for a couple of days. After one sniff of the brisk air on a September morn, an overweight lawyer will suddenly imagine that he is Honest Abe, the Railsplitter. He wants to rush out and chop up a couple of cords of wood. I turned such a character over to Larry one morning. They made kindling out of a couple of lawn chairs that I was going to repair. Then Larry got the sharp little saw which we used for fine carpentry work, led our visitor over to the pile of cedar logs that I had set aside for fence posts and they began to turn out fireplace logs. The girls were always eager to show our guests how to hoe the garden, in spite of the fact that none of them could tell a weed from a bean sprout.

Once, a pair of wonderful fellows who had been friends of Connie's family stopped at our place to rest over on a journey from one place to another. One of them was a business man, but the other was an engineer who worked in some advanced field. I got the impression that he stuffed atoms into bombs or tuned up the engines of rocket ships. After a few restless hours around our place, he hit upon the idea of making a few repairs that I hadn't gotten around to yet.

I tried to divert him, by sending him off with Lynn to meet the pet goat she had trained to shake hands. But he was back soon, eager to get on with the job—any job, that is. He suggested first that he repair a living room lamp which had a frayed cord.

Now Dad, our standing week-end guest, could usually do enough damage repairing things around the place to keep me busy for the week. I did not really feel the need of any additional outside talent. But, since this engineer seemed to be licensed to set off high explosives on five continents, I decided that he might be competent to fix a lamp cord.

When I acceded to his suggestion, he produced a tool kit elaborate enough to have brought a gasp of envy from the owner of any hardware store. Within a short time, he had replaced the cord and was quite happy. Then he discovered a light fixture on our bedroom wall which required surgical attention. As a matter of fact, it had been fixed five times within the last two months: twice by Dad, twice by me, and once by an electrician. But it seemed to have some congenital weakness.

He wrapped this job up in short order and then his eye fell upon my garden tractor.

"Nice little machine," he said. "How does it run?"

"Fine," I replied. "Except it overheats a little."

"Magneto must need adjusting," he said eagerly.

Before I could wiggle my jaw, he had started stripping down the motor. He delivered a learned discourse on each of
216

the dozens of parts he was removing. He managed to put it back together, to my great surprise, and invited me to pull the starter cord. I pulled the cord for fifteen or twenty minutes. Of course nothing happened. So my guest decided he would just have to take the whole thing apart again.

While all this work was going on, the business man was hanging around looking like a lost soul. He had inspected Larry's train, seen Lynn's goat count its age with its paw— (this didn't take too long, since the goat was only a year old)—had been introduced to all of Janie's dolls named Tweenie and had talked over old times with both Claire and Cynthia.

But with the rest of us working as mechanics, he felt left out of it. Finally, I saw him pick up a couple of tools and wander off, like a man with some definite purpose. But when I heard him enter the bathroom a few seconds later, I stopped worrying.

The engineer had now taken the motor apart for the third time. He gave his undivided, thermonuclear attention to the job for another half hour, but still the motor wouldn't start. About this time, the business man reappeared.

"Fixed your toilet," he said to me.

"Fine," I said, without mentioning the fact that we hadn't even noticed that anything was the matter with it.

"Say, we've got to be getting back to town," he reminded the engineer. "We've got a date for dinner, you know."

"Gee, that's right," the engineer said, with as much relief in his voice as if someone had told him that his ten-year stretch on the rock pile was finished.

He began to pack his tools and said to me:

"Sorry I couldn't get this fixed for you."

217

"Well," I said, looking at the dead motor. "At least, it's not overheating any more."

The local handy man, who couldn't explain the function of a single part in the tractor, put it together for me in fifteen minutes that afternoon and it ran just fine.

In the evening, I settled down to read a pamphlet on cranberry cultivation. I turned the switch on the light our friend had fixed, but nothing issued forth except a deep shade of utter darkness.

"Oh, well," I muttered to Connie. "At least, we got the bedroom light fixed. It does work, doesn't it?"

"Sure, and the toilet works, too."

We were awakened out of a sound sleep that night by the noise of a sharp explosion. We sat up in bed to find sparks shooting out of the wall behind the repaired light fixture. The short circuit blew a few fuses along the way.

"I wonder," Connie said sleepily, "what time the toilet is set to explode?"

"Don't worry about that," I said. "The engineer was a highly trained man who understood all the theories. The man who fixed the toilet had never seen a plumbing tool before. I'm sure it'll work forever."

We went to the store the next morning to get materials to repair the repairs of the day before. When we got back to the house, Connie uttered a little squeal as she opened the front door. There was a sizable stream of water, babbling merrily across the living-room floor. I waded upstream toward the bathroom, where I found the toilet gushing like a Texas oil well.

"Knowledge of a subject," I admitted to Connie later, "is not necessarily the handicap I had supposed."

218

But in drawing up our standards of perfection for guests, Connie and I insisted that the ideal visitor must be helpful to some degree. The sort of assistance which was most welcome, on a busy week end, was that which could be rendered around the kitchen sink. Our children never considered drinking water out of the same glass twice. This meant that even without company in the house, they could dirty a couple of dozen glasses from one meal through the next. When we had guests, the stack of dirty dishes could get truly monumental. So Connie always welcomed a couple of extra hands in the soap suds —even if it did mean spending the rest of the week trying to find out where a guest dish-dryer had put the top part of the coffee pot.

One week end, we finally hit the jack-pot in this department. A friend of mine from Army days walked in with his wife. He soon proclaimed that he was going to do all the dishes that were dirtied during his stay. This was a side of his nature that was new to me. I asked a few questions about the domestication of this former second lieutenant. His wife explained that, while some men collect stamps or overstuffed blondes as a hobby, this boy's passion and weakness was washing and drying dishes.

"Now if you are related to Dr. Freud," she said, "please do not ask me why this is. All I know is that it's wonderful."

This guest hardly got out of the kitchen for the rest of the week end. By the time he had polished up the dishes left from one meal, it was time to start on another pile. We sent in relief parties every hour on the hour, but he resolutely drove them away.

"Haven't had so much fun since I was a kid," he said Sunday

219

morning, as he started to work on the glassware and crockery left over from Saturday night's television party.

The rest of us had a fairly easy week end, but my friend looked a little peaked by the time he was ready to leave.

Connie and I congratulated ourselves on our find. It wasn't long after this that we got a wistful little thank-you-ma'am note from his wife. In passing, she said that he hadn't dunked a dirty dish since he'd left our place and she wasn't sure that he ever would again.

But, after months of work and experimentation, we felt finally that we had trained the perfect guest. In some ways, it had been a hard job.

Our candidate for the title was a man who had warned us against trying to live in the country. He declared frequently that he had been out of the big city only once since he had reached voting age. This lone fall from urban grace had left him so shaken that he had vowed never to set foot off concrete again. It took several months of elaborate plotting with his wife before we could lure him down to our place for the week end.

In this life, I try to act as missionary for no cause—including the Back-to-the-Soil Movement. I took no overt steps that week end to convert our friend to my way of life. He followed me around, observed the sort of work that Jack and I were doing and asked a number of questions. Naturally, I was flattered when he told us he had enjoyed the visit so much that he wanted to spend part of his vacation with us.

During this week's holiday, he made himself extremely useful. He helped me take care of the animals. He weeded the garden and he turned the compost heap. He helped Connie with the dishes and got up early enough to have coffee ready

220

for me. He set such a good example for Jack that it was like having three extra hired hands around the place. Both Connie and I were enchanted and we almost joined the girls in shedding tears when he went back to the city.

"At last," Connie sighed, "the perfect guest. We'll have to get them down as often as possible."

A few days later, we got a happy letter from him. I read it and shook my head sadly.

"Dear," I told Connie. "We'll just have to begin all over again training the perfect guest."

"What's happened," she demanded anxiously.

"Bill's put his city house up for sale and is going to buy a little farm. He wants me to be sure and send him instructions for making compost by the Indore Method."

Chapter 21

W HE N the seed catalogues came early in the spring, Jack and I fell to ordering with wild abandon. We bought at least a sample of every vegetable known to grow in the Western Hemisphere and maybe a few that wouldn't.

Jack's enthusiasm for new horticultural undertakings was unbounded. One day, Connie discovered a number of strange sprouts in the flower pots where she kept her geraniums. She was about to weed them out when Jack rushed up with a horrified cry and restrained her.

"Them's our orange and grapefruit trees," he protested. "I'm startin' them from seed."

"I guess the geraniums will just have to go, dear," I laughed. "Unless you think we can get juice for breakfast from them."

Around our way, of course, everyone grew a little something. Most people had a garden, a few chickens and perhaps a pig or a cow—even if they didn't actually own a farm. There was a definite breakdown between the professional farmers, who made their living from the soil; the semi-pros, like myself, who made a living so they could indulge their tastes in farming; and the amateurs, who just wanted some vegetables for the table. The professionals looked upon the rest of us with an amused tolerance. But in the ranks of the semi-pros and amateurs there was a rivalry of the deadliest sort.

When I was new at the game, I used to get pretty discouraged about my efforts whenever I talked to the neighbors. It appeared that I was the only one who ever had trouble with drought, insects or failures of any kind. If I mentioned proudly, early in the spring, that I had just picked my first mess of string beans, some other gardener would let me know that he had been gathering his for two weeks.

One night, I went to visit a friend who was also a semi-professional farmer.

"Just finished eating one of our watermelons," he said, stretching his arms. "Sweet as sugar. Darn thing must have weighed thirty-five pounds."

I was impressed. It had been a dry summer and none of my melons had ripened. I just couldn't understand his success.

But a week or so later, I happened to be passing a store when I saw his wife carrying a freshly purchased watermelon out to the car. Then it was that I got a new perspective on the art of gardening. Thinking back over the successes which my neighbors had been reporting to me, I concluded that there were a lot more gardeners with green tongues than green thumbs.

Little by little, I completed my initiation and learned to understand the devious ways of the local gardeners who were, by and large, bigger liars than the local fishermen. The first summer that Connie and I were married, we were at the home of the friend who had talked such a big watermelon that time. A week-end gardener from Washington was there also, trying

223

to make some progress in the local liars' league. This innocent was bragging about how successful he had been in raising green peas. I sat back to watch my friend carve him up.

"Put many peas in your freezer?" my friend asked casually.

"Boy, I'll say," replied the upstart. "We put up thirteen quarts."

Right then, I knew that my friend had him. The week ender had made the mistake of mentioning a definite figure.

"How much seed did you plant?" my friend asked quickly.

"Oh, I planted a couple of pounds of seed," the innocent replied.

"I only got half a pound of seed planted this year," my friend said in a tone of deceptive deference.

But then he drew his snickersnee and prepared to deliver the coup de grace.

"Honey," he called to his wife, who was out in the kitchen and for all I know opening a can of peas she'd bought at the store, "how many quarts of peas did you put in the freezer this year?"

"Twenty," came the prompt reply.

On the way home, I couldn't help but comment to Connie upon the fine spirit of teamwork which existed between my friend and his wife.

"I hope you'll always remember to back up my stories that way," I said to the bride.

But Connie remained completely naive about the whole thing. When Jack and I planted the garden in the spring, it was naturally a matter of pride for us to be able to get up the first lettuce or radishes around the neighborhood—or at least, to be in a position to imply that we had.

One day, before we had picked our struggling young crop,

Connie came home from a visit with one of our neighbors who was noted as a blatant and unprincipled operator in local green-tongue circles. When Jack saw that she had a bag filled with young lettuce and radishes, he let out a yowl.

"Boss, she's ruined us," he cried.

"What's the matter?" she asked in astonishment.

"Did you, by any chance, tell that guy that we hadn't picked any lettuce or radishes yet?" I asked, with mock severity.

"Sure. Then he said they'd been eating them until they were sick of them and he'd be glad to let me have some for a salad."

I looked at the samples.

"I've got a garden full of stuff that's as ready as this," I said.

"Now he'll be trampin' down here all summer with his big mouth and tellin' us how to raise an early garden," Jack said.

"The only way we could shut him up would be to palm off some of our early tomatoes on his wife," I told Jack.

"You know he's got her trained better 'an to take 'em," he replied. "We're licked. It's disgustipatin'."

Our plan for the summer ahead was to raise enough vegetables so that we could freeze a year's supply. Connie and I figured that we would want to repeat our vegetables about every ten days. I planted seed enough to raise a year's supply of eight or nine vegetables. We thought we would have fresh salad or buy some vegetable that didn't freeze well to fill in the other day or two in our ten-day cycle.

In addition to the vegetables, we began freezing apples, plums, rhubarb, strawberries, blackberries and a few peaches and cherries. For our meat supply, we were growing chickens —in all shapes, sizes and forms—ducks and turkeys, which we planned to freeze. We had our oyster bed in operation

225

now and, as the weather warmed, we began catching crabs and fish to freeze.

Connie persuaded me to take her fishing one evening. I assured her that it was no sport for a beginner. We stayed out for a couple of hours and she caught seven big fish. I was so busy baiting her hooks and taking off the fish that I didn't even register a bite. But when I told her that it was the unwritten law of fishing that everyone cleaned his own catch, she decided she wouldn't go any more.

As our cache of food mounted, we found that our ten-cubic foot freezer was inadequate. We began to rent lockers in a freezer plant and I looked at my bills one day to discover that we were paying sixty dollars a year for locker space.

This revelation led me to a complete checkup on the expenses involved in operating the homestead. The Brave Pioneer, who had set out to live off the land, was spending money to the tune of about one hundred dollars a month on the farm, I discovered. This did not include the cost of feeding Jack, a staggering sum which I preferred to keep a secret from myself.

Since any examination of expenses always depresses me, I began to ruinate upon the wisdom of the whole operation. I sat down and thumbed through the book on how to live cheaply on a little piece of land. I chuckled ironically as I saw a couple of the chapter headings—such as "Your Own Milk Supply." I was feeding four goats now, none of which was producing a drop of milk at the moment. Then I came to "Your Own Little Sugar Factory," and thought bitterly of how the bees had scrammed out on me after all the trouble I had gone to in making a happy home for them.

There were a few things about homesteading, I concluded, that the book hadn't covered. I was now spending two-thirds of my working time trying to lick the farming problem. It was costing me so much money that I actually had to spend more writing time earning money—to pay for the things that were going to save me money.

But, being stubbornly optimistic about the entire undertaking, I shrugged away these melancholy thoughts.

"I'll get back all of this investment, in the years to come," I told myself.

This conclusion, of course, was based upon the assumption that we could keep working like this for years to come. But the way the rest of the family was taking to homesteading, I sometimes doubted that we would be able to finish out the summer.

When the big crop of spinach was ready to pick, we began to haul it in by the bushel basket for Connie to freeze. The vegetable had to be blanched in boiling water before being packaged. I came upon my bride in the kitchen one hot afternoon. Her hair was stringy, her nose was red and she was soaked with perspiration. She looked as if her morale needed a boost, so I gave her a kiss and a small pep talk which wound up with the moral:

"See how cheap it is to live in the country?"

"It may be cheap," she retorted, lifting a colander full of limp and steaming spinach out of the water, "but I ask you —is it living?"

The children were given to this same sort of enthusiasm for the hard, unpleasant tasks which were assigned to them.

Baseball season was on and Larry's current obsession was keeping up with the major leagues. Any work around the farm which interfered with his watching the game on television was construed by him to be a crime against humanity.

227

The girls scattered in all directions when I needed anyone to pull weeds, pick spinach or shell peas. I really felt sorry for them. Because as a child, I hadn't been put to work in the fields during the summer—even for the little time I required of our kids.

"I'll catch ammonia maybe and really get sick, prob'ly," Claire complained to me one day when she was weeding the strawberries.

"Claire, don't you wish we was million-ears and could have maids to pull the weeds for us," Janie suggested.

My own children had worked around the place before and they had some experience at it. But neither Cynthia nor Claire had been forced to perform involuntary servitude of any sort before they came to Dukehart. I don't know whether it was the chores or real homesickness which touched it off, but they suddenly began talking a lot about their old home.

"Does the kajooma man come around here, Daddy?" Cynthia asked.

"The what?" I said.

"The kajooma man—you know, that sells ice cream."

"I'm afraid not," I said.

"He used to come around every night after supper and we'd all run out with our dimes," she said wistfully, pulling up another blade of grass.

I decided that the girls would enjoy their work more if I paid them for it. So I worked out a wage rate for them and then they were a little happier about the whole thing.

Claire came to me one day and said:

"Me'n Cynthia is savin' our money, for we can go back and see our grandmothers."

"Okay," I said. "We'll see if you can't make a visit up

there this year. And I'm glad to see you saving something, instead of blowing it all on bubble gum."

"Yeah. I'm doin' it for you told me it was good to save."

"I always save my money," Janie said proudly.

"Well, *you* ought to spend some of it sometimes," I said. "Don't be a little miser."

"But, if I spend it, Daddy, I won't have it," she said.

"Look at Daddy," I said unhappily. "I've been saving my money all my life, and I still haven't got any."

By now, my two-acre plot was a miniature farm on which I duplicated almost all the processes of the professional farmers. I worked at it like a man possessed by the gambling fever or bitten by the gold bug, but somehow the rest of the family just didn't quite fit into the frame I had built. In spite of my numerous failures, I was being reasonably successful at producing according to the homesteading plan. But the place wasn't supporting me—I was supporting it. We were still suburbanites, not Pioneers.

One day, Lynn and Cynthia came home, almost too excited to talk, and informed us that a ballet class was being formed. A professional dancer was coming down from Washington to give lessons once a week. The tuition for Lynn and Cynthia was not small and, in addition, there would be the time and expense involved in transporting them a considerable distance for the lessons.

"Gee, they're excited about it, aren't they?" Connie said.

"I'm against it," I said flatly.

"It would teach them grace and poise," she said.

"They could learn that husking corn, if they wanted to."

"But they don't like to husk corn. They want to dance."

"Look, Dear," I said quietly. "I think this is about where

we should look things in the eye. If we were city people, it would be different. . . ."

"But we are city people," she said gently.

"Are we? I'm trying to be a farmer. I want to live simply. I don't need all these frills. But I can't do it all alone. It's a family business."

She looked at me thoughtfully for a moment, but said nothing.

A few days later, while visiting at the home of a neighbor, we met a couple about our age who owned a tobacco farm in the county. As everyone did, they took to Connie immediately and, before the evening was over, we had accepted an invitation to visit them.

A few nights later, as we drove toward their farm, I said to my bride:

"Now you'll see how a real farm family lives."

"This is what you want for us?" she asked.

"Well," I said, a little evasively, "it's a good, honest way of life. These people aren't breaking their necks to buy New York clothes or get the kids' teeth perfectly straight. They work together and they're happy. They've got a boy Larry's age who does a man's work. And their little girls work in the fields and don't grumble about it."

In a short time, we approached a plain, roomy farmhouse, surrounded by a stand of old trees. There was no television antenna on the roof. I parked our car behind a late-model, pickup truck which I knew was this family's only vehicle.

Our friends ushered us into the living room. The floor was covered with a clean, linoleum rug which was hardly faded at all. The room was filled with dark, solid furniture which was intended, obviously, not to please the eye but to give long, comfortable service.

The conversation was a little slow in getting started, but before long everyone was feeling at ease. I tested a couple of remarks upon politics and the war situation, but soon switched to chickens and hogs. I listened as the farmer talked about his problems in raising tobacco, while Connie and his wife talked about children. The son of the family was listening to murder mysteries on the radio, as the girls, clean and healthy looking in their little home-made dresses, read comic books.

From time to time, the wife would excuse herself to go to the kitchen to check up on the bread she had rising or the kettle of soup which stood on the back of the wood-burning stove.

"I was down to the barn strippin' 'bacca most of the day," she apologized. "An' I had such a big wash to do this afternoon that I got behin' in the kitchen. I know the house looks jus' a mess."

She had been darning socks when we arrived, but she had put the work aside. Now her roughened, red hands fluttered nervously with nothing to do. In the harsh light of the room, her face, browned by the sun and wind, looked tired and a little old.

We left early, because we knew that they would all be getting up at daybreak to get the chores done.

"Nice people," I said to Connie as we drove home.

"Aren't they though?"

"We'll have to get them to bring their kids down to see television some night."

"It would be a treat for them."

231

"They're really hard workers," I observed.

"They must be."

"Happy together, too."

We drove in silence for a while. Finally, I said:

"Honey, I've been thinking some more about those ballet lessons for the girls. I guess they ought to have them."

Chapter 22

*O*N E summer night, not long after Connie and I had celebrated the first anniversary of our wedding, we decided to see a movie in Leonardtown. We left Jack in charge of the children and arrived at the theater for the last show. It was the movie of Scott Fitzgerald's *The Great Gatsby* and, as good pictures sometimes do, it left me under its spell.

As we left the theater shortly after eleven o'clock and started the thirteen-mile ride home, I was haunted by the memory of Gatsby, with blood pouring from his wound, slipping back into his ornate swimming pool. I fell into a mood of melancholy introspection as we bounced along the narrow, lonely road. I fell to musing aloud and Connie listened without interruption.

"Somehow," I said wearily, "I've lost my way in life. I've always known where I wanted to go and what I wanted to do. But I've gotten all mixed up, since I started out to be the Brave Pioneer. I'm running as fast as I can, but I just don't know where I'm going."

We were about half way home when ahead, on the road

which had been completely deserted until now, we saw a cluster of headlights. I stopped the car, finding the road blocked completely in both directions. Peering out of the window I could see that two automobiles had been involved in what appeared to be a minor accident.

Some sort of fight was taking place and, as I watched, the outlines became somewhat clearer. The occupants of one of the cars, which had been traveling toward us, were Negroes. The men in the other car were white and acted as if they had been drinking heavily. The white men were beating the Negro driver and threatening others in the car with a jack handle.

It looked like just the sort of thing that I should stay out of, so I stuck close to my car. But when I saw one of the white men reach into the Negro's car and smash his fist into the driver's face, I began to get angry. I blew my horn and shouted up past the cars in front of me, hoping that this might help break up the senseless battle.

A few seconds later, the Negro's car started toward us and, as it pulled past my car, I could see that the driver's face was bleeding badly. The car went thirty or forty feet beyond us and then stopped. The road ahead was still blocked by other cars and another automobile had pulled up behind mine.

I decided not to get mixed up in the little riot which seemed to be continuing up ahead, on the theory that if anyone was going to be hit on the head with a jack handle, it would surely be me. Then my eye fell upon the injured Negro's car behind me. It occurred to me that the man might need help and, on a sudden impulse, I wheeled and walked toward his car to offer my assistance.

It was dark as I approached his car from behind. I thought I had better make it clear that I was approaching in a friendly
234

spirit and so, as I reached the rear fender of the car, I called out in a quiet tone:

"Say, fellow . . ."

Suddenly, the car door swung open and the driver took a quick step toward me. Without speaking, he lunged at me and I felt a heavy blow on the right side of my chest.

"I was only trying to help you," I protested, as he jumped back into the car and raced away.

I turned and started to walk back to the car where Connie was waiting. I shook my head sadly as I walked, and felt sorry at the realization that the Negro had gone away before I could make him understand that the hand of at least one white man was being offered in friendship. I wondered why my chest hurt so from the force of the blow.

All the other cars which had been clustered around the scene had departed now, except the one which was behind mine. Two young men were standing beside it, waiting for me to move. As I passed them, one of them cried out:

"Look, he's been cut."

In a panic, I put my hand to my chest and brought it away sticky with warm blood. The boys rushed to my side, helped me to my car and opened the door. As Connie saw the spreading blood stain on my white shirt front, she let out an agonized cry.

"I'm hurt, dear," I said in fright.

"Is it bad?" she asked quickly.

Suddenly, the pain in my chest was excrutiating. I grew terribly weak. I could hardly draw a breath and when I tried, it felt as if something sharp were being driven into my lung.

"You've got to help me," Connie cried out to the two youngsters.

I could feel her trembling on the seat beside me as one of the boys started our car. There was a brief debate as to whether they should drive me to the hospital in Leonardtown or to the home of an elderly country doctor a mile or so down the road. I told them to get me to the doctor, for I didn't feel that I would live to reach the hospital. We were there in a minute and they half-carried me into the office and laid me down on the worn, linoleum-covered floor. The boys immediately ordered an ambulance to take me to the hospital.

Connie kneeled beside me, sobbing, and I could feel her tears fall on my face. The doctor came in and stood over us.

I was now slipping away toward unconsciousness, but I could not quite make it. Every time I would gasp for a little air, it would cause such pain that I would be brought back to the horrible world of reality. A strange jumble of thoughts began to flood in on me. At first, I could think only of the irony of the whole thing . . . dying on the floor of a country doctor's office . . . through a whole stinking war, from Normandy to Berlin, without a scratch . . . and coming home from the movies on a Sunday night with my wife and I get it on a quiet country road . . . trying to help somebody out . . . and I get it. The whole thing suddenly struck me as amusing.

"What's he smiling about?" the doctor demanded.

I just shook my head and smiled. The world was retreating farther from me, now. I knew only that Connie's lovely face was close to mine. Suddenly, I realized that I was at death's door. I felt that I would pass through it in a matter of seconds, or minutes. I felt a surge of panic. The memory of all of the things I had hoped to do and hoped to be in life flooded upon me. In a flash, I was full of bitter, hateful remorse. It was too late, now.

But then I realized that it was too late for remorse, even. It did not matter now. It was over. My life was done. Now I'd know the riddle of death. Or I would know nothing. I relaxed. I was dying, I told myself. And, except for Connie, I just didn't care.

Finally the ambulance came and I winced with pain as they lifted me on the stretcher. Then I was in the emergency room of the little county hospital and a nurse was asking:

"What's he smiling about?"

They got me out of my clothes, shot me full of blood plasma and morphine and found a doctor to work over me. At one point, I glanced down at the right side of my chest and saw my wound, like a tiny mouth, gushing blood as I struggled to breath.

I awakened in a strange room in the morning. I was surprised to even awaken, so convinced had I been that I was dying. But I felt as if I were strangling and no one came to help me. Finally, I looked up to see Connie and Jack standing in the room.

The doctor who had treated me upon my arrival at the hospital appeared some time later and advised Connie to have me moved by ambulance to the Johns Hopkins Hospital in Baltimore.

"This hospital just isn't equipped to handle a case this serious," he said soberly.

Connie had called Mother and she was on her way to Dukehart to look after the children. Within the hour, I was in the ambulance shrieking along the country roads that led to Baltimore, eighty-five miles away. Connie sat beside my stretcher, holding my hand.

We arrived at Hopkins at the same moment as some thirteen people who had been scraped up off the pavements after a bad automobile accident. For a while, the doctors were so busy trying to sort out these people's parts and restore them to the rightful owners that I didn't get much attention.

But Connie moved around the hospital like a little fury and finally the wheels began to turn. I was x-rayed, blood typed, transfused, hypoed and finally delivered to a clean bed in a big ward. I was now in just about the best hospital in the world, I told myself, and safe.

For the first time, I decided that I was going to live.

But that, Connie told me later, was more than the doctors would promise her.

I was moved into a room which I had to myself that evening. My left arm, full of holes where needles had gone in during the afternoon, was strapped to a board. A needle, carrying glucose into my veins, was inserted in this arm. Connie's strong little hands were holding my other arm as I went to sleep that night.

She was there when I opened my eyes in the morning.

"I guess I'll live, after all," I whispered. "No double indemnity for you."

Connie leaned over and kissed me gently.

Chapter 23

TH E days that followed were like a dream in the twilight, during which peace followed pain and pain followed peace. Always, Connie seemed to be at my side. Sometimes she read aloud to me or talked. Sometimes, she would sit in silence for an hour, just holding my hand. Then the drab little room seemed beautiful, and alive with love.

My progress was slow and made half-maddening by a number of painful medical practices required to clear the blood out of my right lung. The knife had punctured the lung and the blade had missed one of the main arteries into my heart by less than an inch.

"You would never have gotten this far, if it had hit the artery," the doctor said cheerfully. "You're a very lucky man."

The infection which had followed the wound subsided gradually, and the doctors took me off the critical list. I finally suggested to Connie, after she had spent ten days at my bedside, that she go home for a visit.

She came back the next day, bearing messages of good cheer from the children.

"How's everything on the farm?" I asked.

"Fine. Phyllis had twin kids again."

"What about the turkeys?"

"Good news. You lost one."

"What's so good about that?"

"Jack opened its gizzard and found my diamond."

"The hens laying?"

"They must be. The children say they've been living on eggs."

"How's Mother holding up?"

"Fine. Except Jack won't speak to her."

"What's eating him?"

"He's worrying about you. That's just his way of showing it."

"That adds."

"He says he can't stand the strain of working for a man who goes around getting half killed. He's going to quit and join the Army when you get back on your feet. It'll be more peaceable, he says."

"I can take it. But can the Army?"

Twice, during the time I was there, other patients were assigned to share the room with me. Both were young men, who spent twenty-four hours in the room before undergoing delicate surgery. Both of them died and these tragedies deepened the moods of depression which I sometimes felt.

In the dim hours of the hospital night, when sleep would not come, I tried to sort out the pieces of my life. Some I wanted to keep, some I wanted to throw away. For the first time, I realized upon what a slender thread we string our beads of hope. When next I lay down to die, I wanted to be sure that there would be no regret for things left undone.

Neither dreams of fame, nor material advancement, nor

quixotic hopes of helping to save mankind from its own folly figured any longer as important in my scheme of life. What was important was the happiness and security of the family which Connie and I had brought together.

I wondered whether the island and the crazy homesteading project was really the thing the family wanted—or was it simply an escape device created for myself? I still believed I could get a family milk supply from goats and honey from bees. There were more things I wanted to try—geese and pigeons and pigs. But, I convinced myself, I was the only one who wanted this way of life.

I thought of Connie's kids, working in the garden to earn a few dimes so they could get to a city and wait on the street corner for the ice-cream man to tinkle his bell at sunset. I thought of Connie, an artist, denying her talents so that she could put up pickle relish. It wasn't right, I told myself.

One day, while Connie was visiting back home, Dad came to see me at the hospital. He was bright and chipper and obviously had something on his mind. Finally, he came out with it.

"You know, I've worked on that place down there ever since I can remember," he said reflectively. "I always thought that some day I'd be able to retire and do exactly what you're doing now."

"I know," I said. "And I guess we're sort of in your way."

"No. No. But I know now that I'll never be able to do it. It's never going to be anything more than just a week-end place for me. But you're there with your family and I want you to *have* the place. I'm going to turn it over to you and Connie."

"Gosh, Dad, I can't tell you how kind I think that is," I replied slowly. "But I just don't know. I don't know whether we can keep on living there."

I saw a pained expression cross his face.

"I like it," I added quickly. "You know what it means to me. But it's the rest of the family. I just don't think it's the life they want."

He said nothing, but I knew he understood.

"Let me talk to Connie about it," I added.

Connie was back at the hospital the next morning. She bustled into the room, full of excitement.

"I've got a surprise for you," she said.

Suddenly, the door burst open and the children flooded in. They were solemn and wide-eyed, not knowing what to expect for a moment. Then they relaxed and became their normal, uninhibited selves.

"Now you children keep quiet," Connie said sternly. "You know the trouble I had getting you in here at all."

"Hey, listen who's making with the tough discipline, now," I laughed. "Let 'em be themselves."

Larry stood at the door, eyeing the pretty nurses as they walked down the corridor. Lynn came over and leaned on the bed, looking at me with that tender, pitying glance which she usually saved for wounded birds. Claire and Janie hung on the foot of the bed, and Cynthia clung to Connie, as if for protection.

"I think 'at was mean of 'at man to hurt you," Claire said sulkily. "Least, he could of said he's sorry."

"Claire," said Janie reprovingly. "Le's not amind Daddy of it."

Just then, an interne passed by the door with a tray of

needles and medicine. Cynthia hugged Connie tighter and went white.

"They might stick one of those needles in me by mistake," she squeaked.

She recovered quickly and a few minutes later said:

"I've got a joke to tell you, Daddy, if I can remember it."

"Okay," I replied.

"What did the salad dressing say when the maid opened the refrigerator?" she demanded.

"I give up," I said. "I'm too weak to struggle."

"It said: 'Shut the door. I'm mayonnaise.' "

"Not mayonnaise, Cynthia—dressing," Lynn moaned.

"Oh," said Cynthia, looking crestfallen.

"Guess what?" Lynn asked me happily. "My banties have hatched out some little chicks."

"And I've got a mother rabbit, now," Cynthia announced.

"Oh, Daddy," Janie said excitedly, "the little new goats are so beeyoodiful!"

"One of 'em's mine," Claire said proudly. "I named him Peanut."

"Th'other's one's mine," Janie said.

"Well, you girls are certainly full of news about the farm," I observed. "Trying to make me think you like it?"

"Oh, Daddy, don't be silly," said Cynthia. "Of course we love it."

"Tell me," I asked. "Has the kajooma man been around yet?"

"You know there's no kajooma man," Cynthia replied. "Besides, why would we want kajoomas when we can make our very own good ice cream with goat's milk?"

"Did you make ice cream?" I asked Connie in surprise. "Like a real farmer's wife?"

"Yup. Larry fixed the ice-cream freezer for us," she said.

"He did?" I asked incredulously.

"Sure," he replied casually. "Found out what was wrong with that lamp in the living room, too."

"I didn't know you could do anything like that," I laughed.

"Oh, I'm learnin'," he said, as his eyes followed another nurse past the door.

There was a pause.

"Kin we tell him now?" asked Claire.

"Yeah, can we—can we?" chorused the other girls.

"I guess this is a good time," said Connie. "He's strong enough now to stand the shock."

"For God's sake," I demanded. "What is it?"

"You know the money me'n Claire have been saving?" Cynthia asked.

"What you've been saving to visit Grandmother?" I inquired.

"Yeah. Well, guess what we bought?"

"A kajooma truck."

"Daddy! Quit teasing."

"All right, tell me."

"We bought a *pig!*" she fairly shouted.

I looked from one to the other with disbelief. They roared with laughter.

"And Mommy bought one, too," Lynn giggled. "They're called the Duke and Duchess of Dukehart."

"I'm unna git me some of those oh-so-good, pork choppers off mine," Claire said.

"An' Daddy, you know pigs give bacon, too," Cynthia assured me.

I shook my head with wonder as I looked at their happy, healthy faces.

244

"Did you go in on the pig deal with all your money?" I asked Janie.

"All what money, Daddy? That's what I wanna know," she said.

"All that money you've been hoarding and couldn't decide what to buy," I said.

"She started pestering me to take her to the dime store when I was home last time," Connie explained. "She took all her money down there and blew it in."

"What's been going on?" I demanded. "Janie's suddenly turned spendthrift!"

"Least, I got a pig to show for mine," Claire said scornfully.

"Don't werry, Claire," Janie replied. "It's on'y money."

"I guess Jack is happy about the pigs," I said wistfully. "He's nuts about pigs."

"Th' Duke's th' bigges'," Janie said. "He kin even eat more'n Jack."

I looked at my family all laughing around the bed and maybe a couple of tears did roll down my cheeks.

"And I was going to ask you if you wanted to move back to the city," I said.

Everyone looked shocked.

"Daddy," said Janie gravely. "You mus' of gotten cuckoo aroun' this horsepital."

Later in the day, the children went back home with a neighbor of ours who was in town shopping. Connie stayed with me.

"Dad wants to turn the place over to us," I told her. "I guess I'd better let him, huh?"

"You heard what the kids said," she replied.

245

I reached out for her hand.

"You remember the night after we were married, and we made our wish on the moon?" I asked.

She smiled and squeezed my hand.

"Mine came true," I said.

"So did mine," she replied. "Tell me what you wished?"

"I wished that my kids would grow up to be like you," I said.

She leaned down and put her face close to mine.

"And I wished that mine would be just like you," she whispered.